Hey, Andrew! Teach Me Some Greek!

A BIBLICAL GREEK WORKTEXT

LEVEL 1

BY KAREN MOHS

Dear Parent/Teacher:

Welcome to the exciting world of koiné Greek!

This Level One workbook, designed to accompany the reader by the same name, allows the child to learn by doing. Each lesson builds on the previous lesson. Therefore, a systematic approach is recommended.

Daily drill will assist memory and assure success in this study. You may remove the flashcard pages at the end of the workbook, cut out the letters, and copy, paste, or tape them onto 3 by 5 inch cards.

Begin use of flashcards when indicated in the workbook. As the child learns each new letter or word, add it to the flashcard stack. Check the box at the bottom of each page to record and encourage consistency.

A glossary at the end of the workbook defines Greek words used in the letter recognition exercises.

An answer key is available, as well as quizzes/exams and flashcards on a ring. The audio pronunciation CD or cassette tape includes Greek letters, vocabulary, "The Greek Alphabet Song," and a reading of *The Reader*.

Have fun!

References:

New Testament Greek For Beginners by J. Gresham Machen
Essentials of New Testament Greek by Ray Summers
A Short Syntax of New Testament Greek by H.P.V. Nunn
Moods and Tenses of New Testament Greek by Earnest De Witt Burton
A Manual Grammar of the Greek New Testament by Dana and Mantey
Exhaustive Concordance of the Bible by James Strong

ISBN-13: 978-1-931842-01-3
ISBN-10: 1-931842-01-9

Greek 'n' Stuff
P.O. Box 882
Moline, IL 61266-0882
www.greeknstuff.com

Revised 7/07

This workbook
belongs to me:

____

(student's name)

because
I'M LEARNING GREEK!

TABLE OF CONTENTS

Appendix

ALPHA

(Put your pencil here and trace the letter.)

Write the letter *alpha* across each line.
As you write it, say "**al**-fa."

More Practice with ALPHA

Alpha sounds like **a** in ***father***.

α

α

α

α

α

α

α

REMEMBER!
Alpha sounds like **a** in ***father***.

Circle the words that have the alpha sound.

cot	great
lark	palm
math	guard
fan	rat
sonic	tame
watch	day
him	jar

LET'S PRACTICE

Make little alphas in this giant alpha.

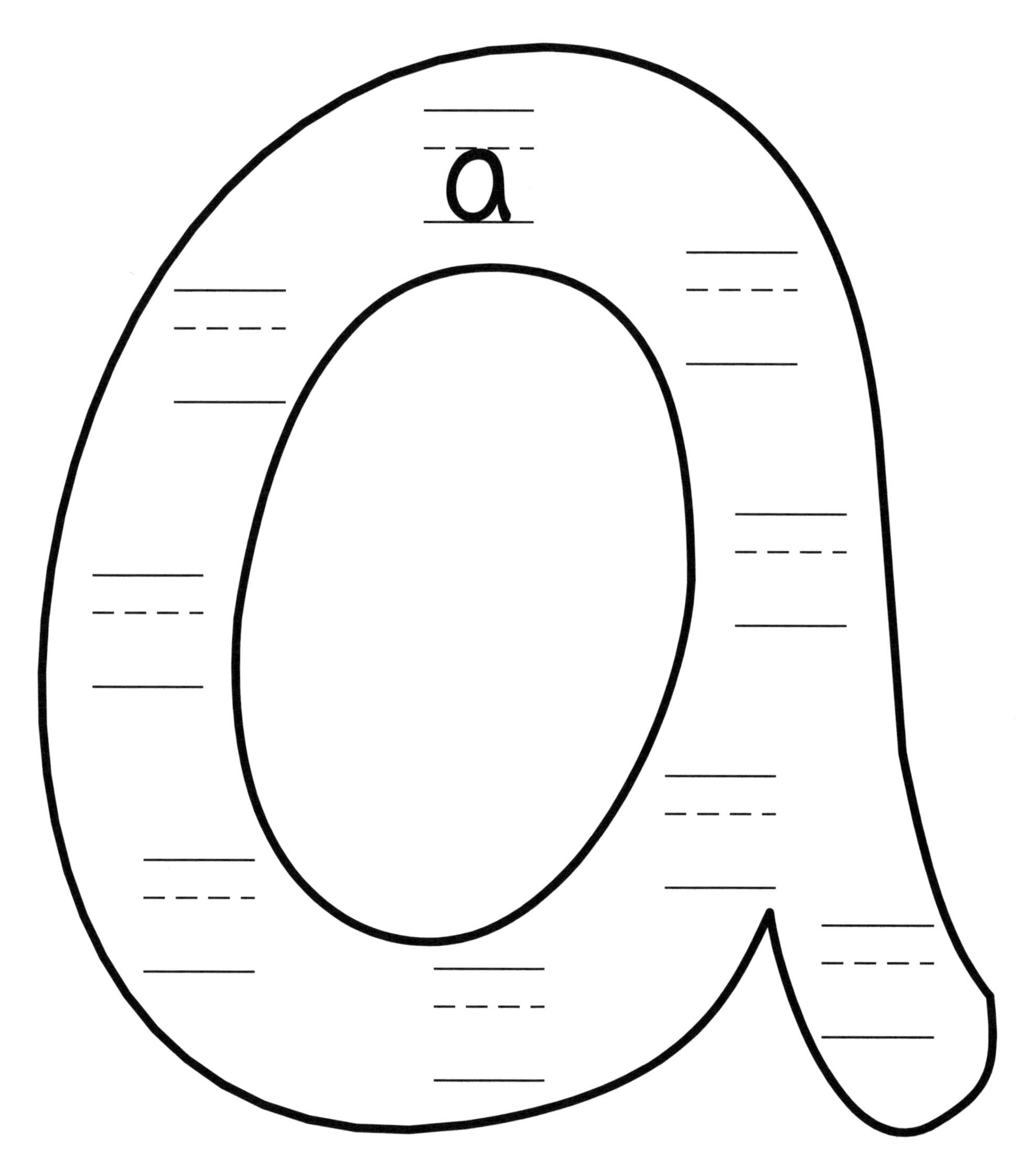

BETA

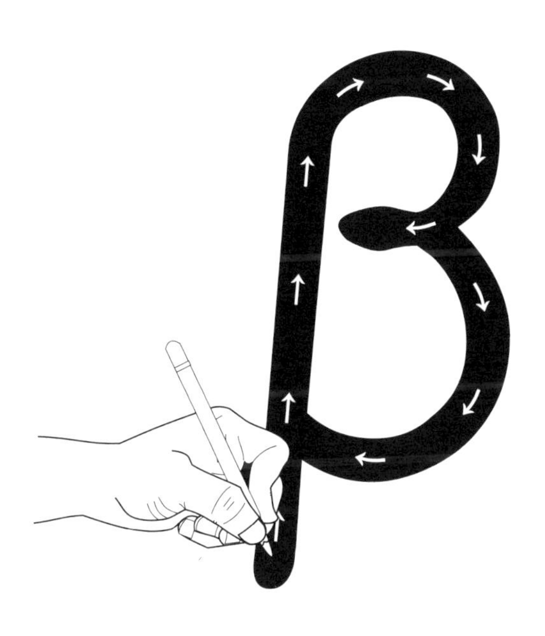

Write the letter *beta* across each line.
As you write it, say "**bay**-ta."

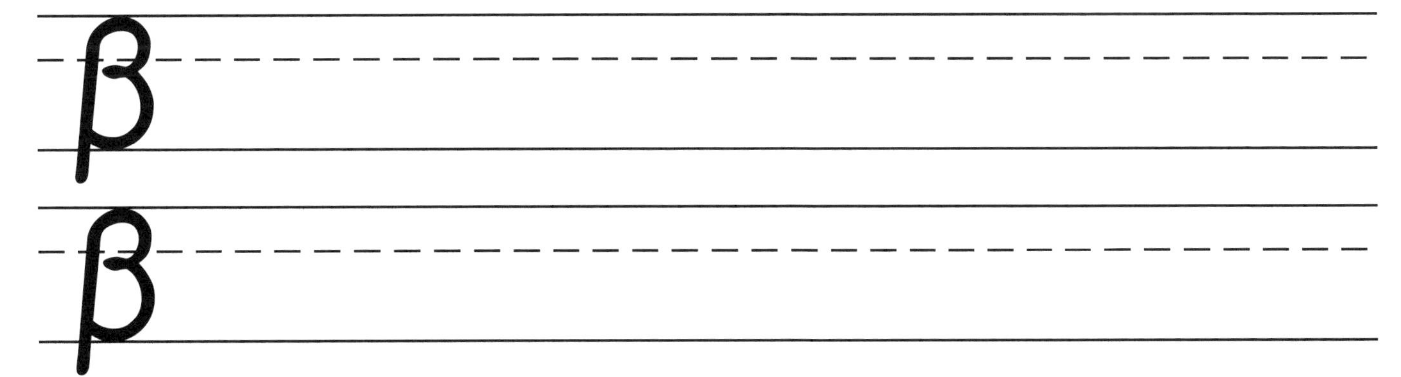

More Practice with BETA

Beta sounds like **b** in ***bat***.

β

β

β

β

β

β

β

LET'S PRACTICE

Draw lines from the words that have the beta sound to the big beta in the middle of the page.

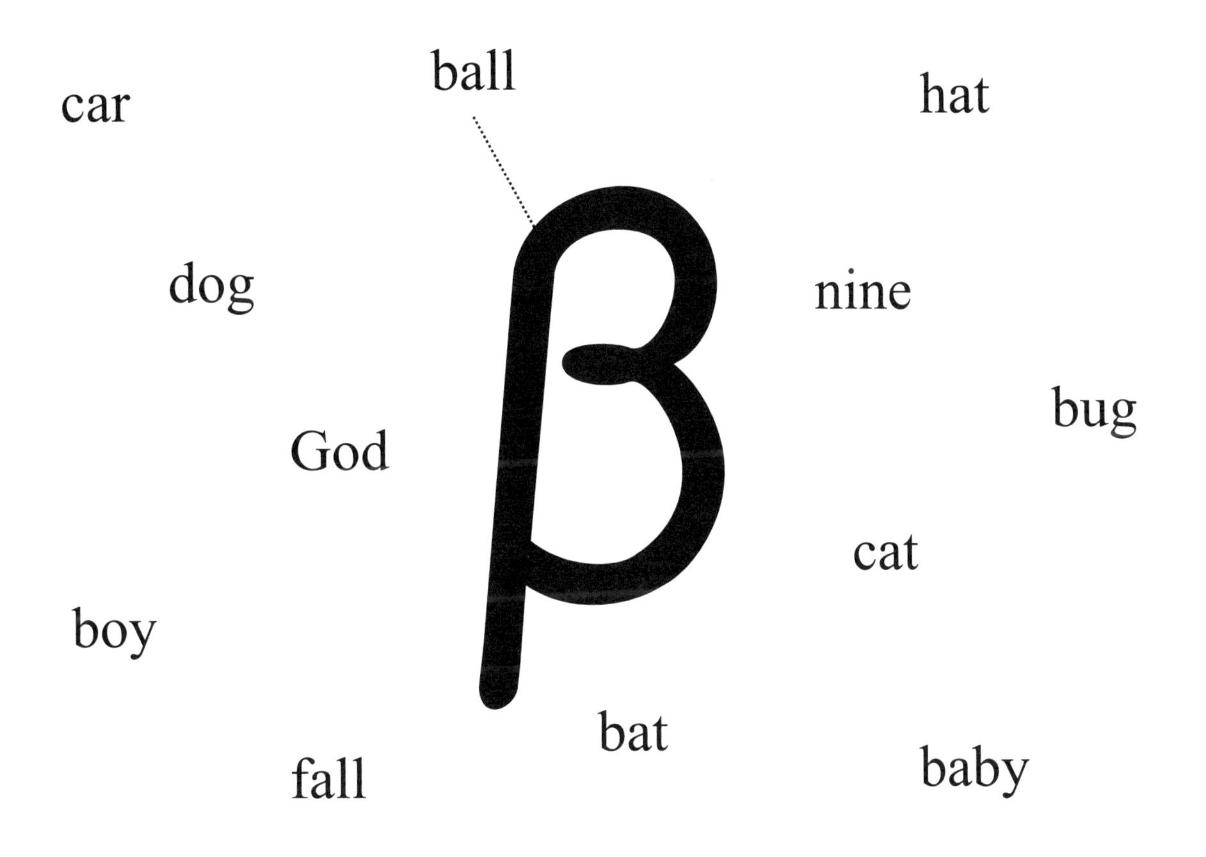

You now know the first two letters of the Greek alphabet. Start your flashcard deck with these letters and practice them every day.

(See back of workbook for flashcards.)

☐ I practiced my flashcards today.

LET'S PRACTICE

Draw lines from the Greek letters to their names.

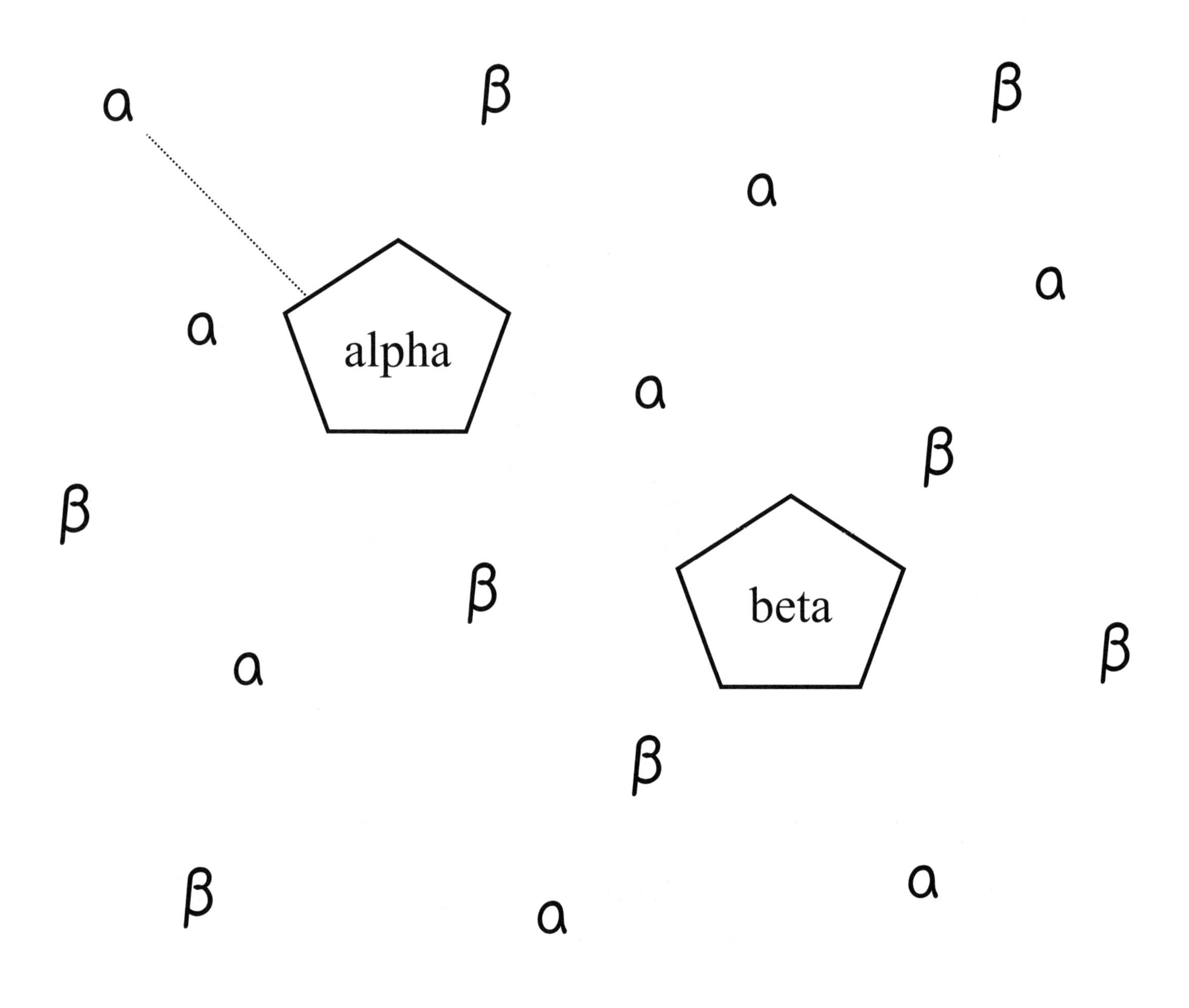

☐ I practiced my flashcards today.

GAMMA

Write the letter *gamma* across each line.
As you write it, say "**gam**-ma."

γ

γ

More Practice
with
GAMMA

Gamma sounds like **g** in ***God***.

γ

γ

γ

γ

γ

γ

☐ I practiced my flashcards today.
(Remember to add this new card to your flashcards.)

LET'S PRACTICE

Write three letters of the Greek alphabet in order.

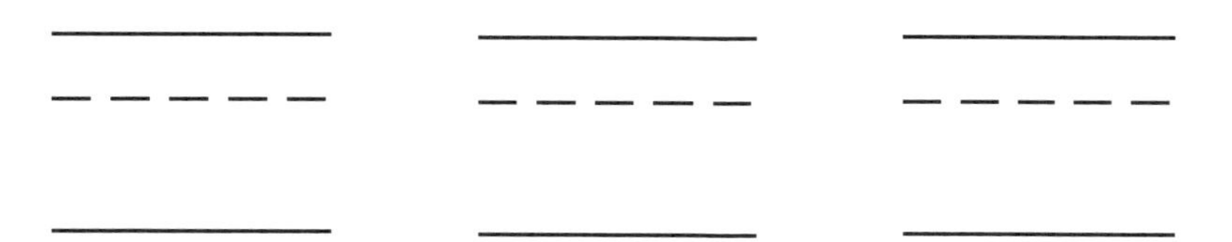

Draw lines from the Greek letters to their names.

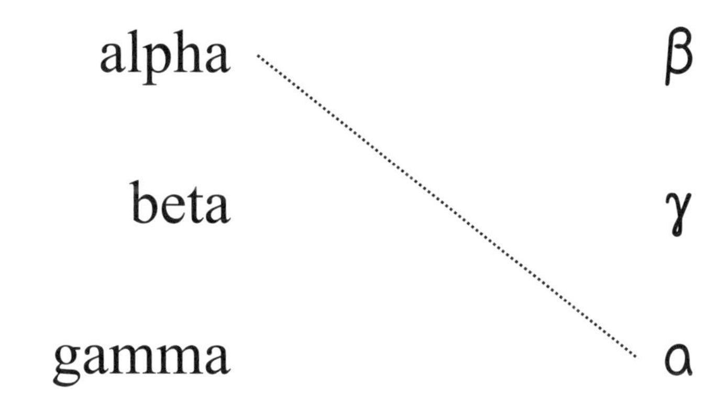

Circle the Greek letters.

g z β j α m γ d c

☐ I practiced my flashcards today.

LET'S PRACTICE

WHAT'S MY SOUND? Draw lines from the Greek letters to the words that have their sounds.

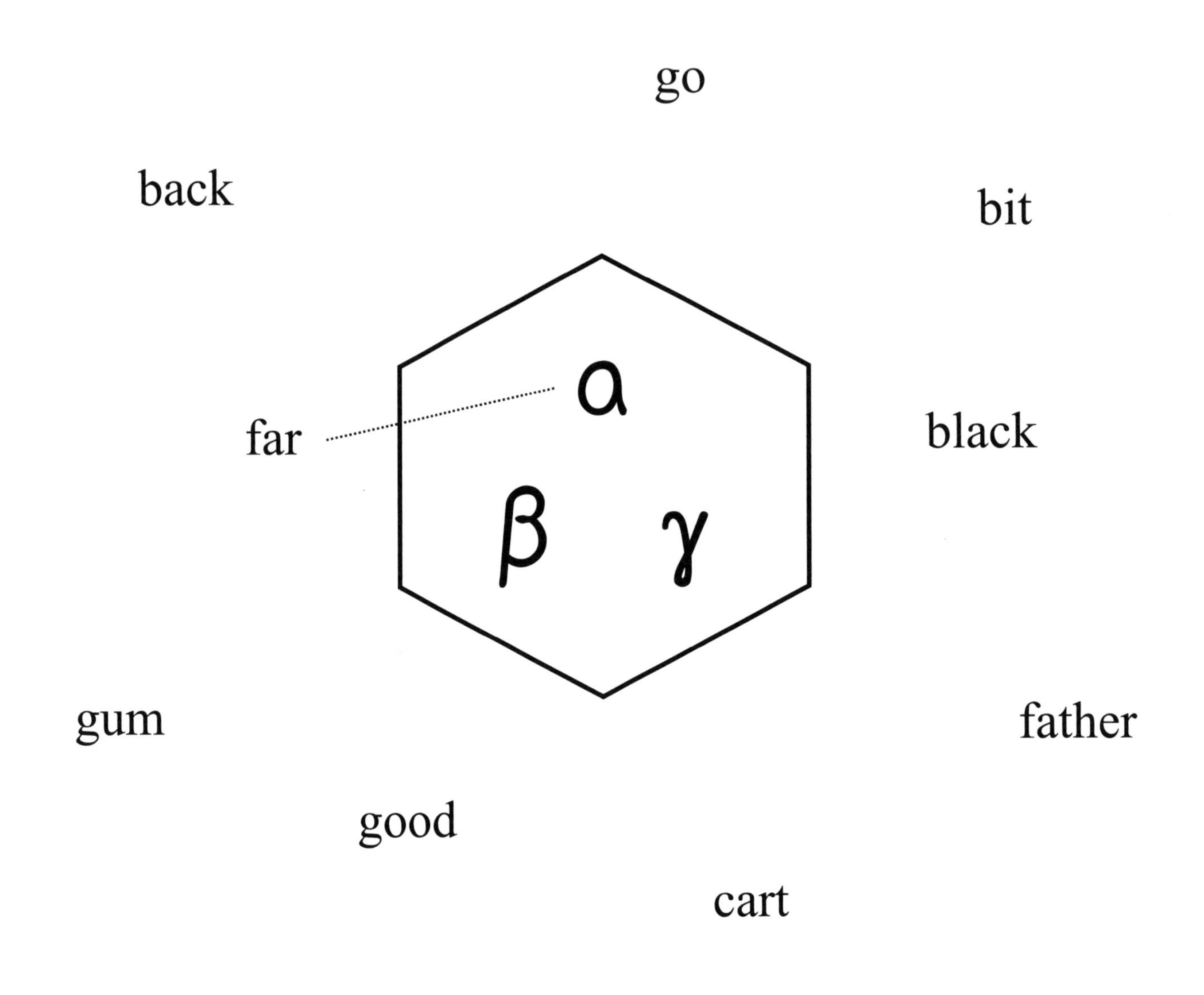

☐ I practiced my flashcards today.

DELTA

Write the letter *delta* across each line.
As you write it, say "**del**-ta."

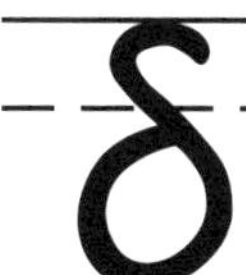

More Practice with DELTA

Delta sounds like **d** in ***dog***.

δ

δ

δ

δ

δ

δ

☐ I practiced my flashcards today.

(Remember to add this new card to your flashcards.)

LET'S PRACTICE

Write four letters of the Greek alphabet in order.

Write the names of the Greek letters.

α ______________

β ______________

γ ______________

δ ______________

Blacken the boxes containing the Greek letters. Then read the message.

β	I	γ	β	L	O	V	E	α	γ	G	R	E	E	K	α

☐ I practiced my flashcards today.

LET'S PRACTICE

Draw lines from the Greek letters to their sounds.

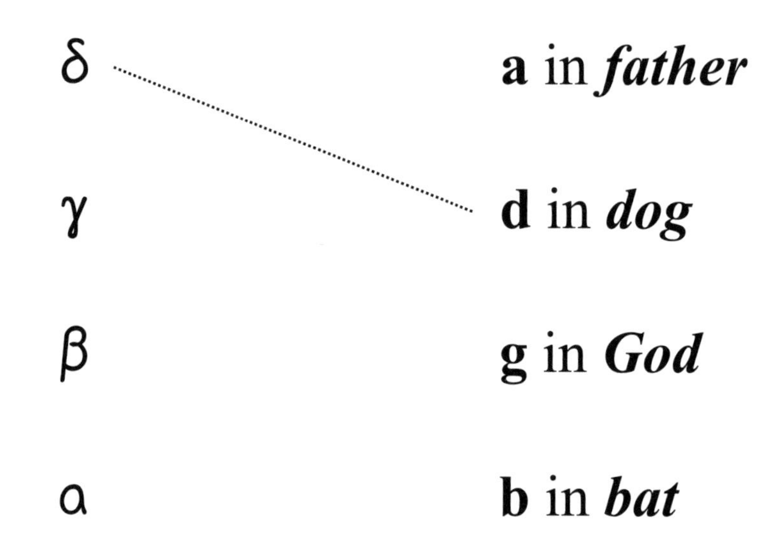

Fill in the missing parts of the Greek letters.

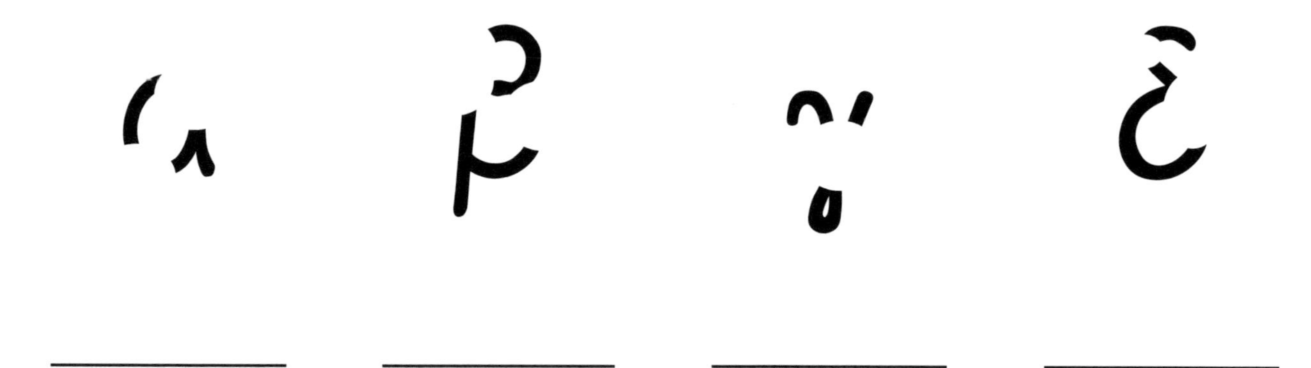

Now write their names on the lines.

☐ I practiced my flashcards today.

EPSILON

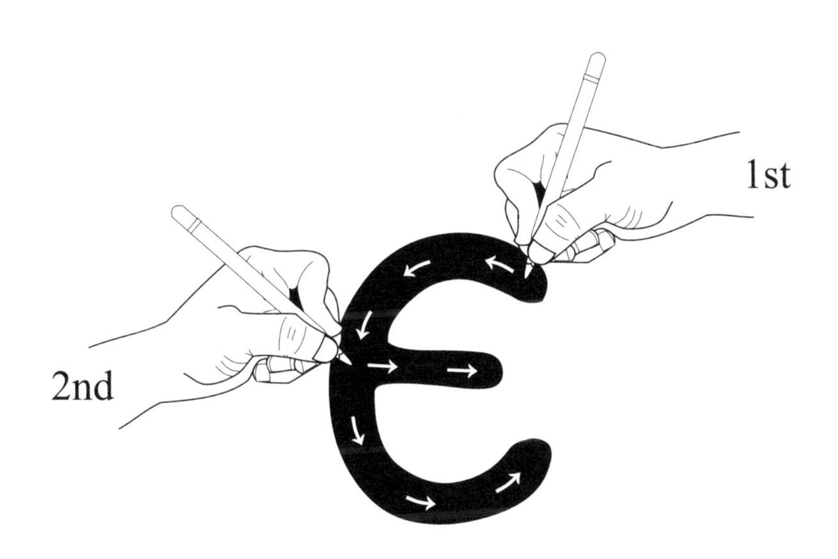

Write the letter *epsilon* across each line.
As you write it, say "**ep**-si-lon."

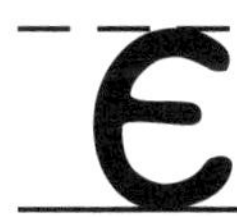

More Practice with EPSILON

Epsilon sounds like **e** in ***get***.

ε

ε

ε

ε

ε

ε

☐ I practiced my flashcards today.
(Remember to add this new card to your flashcards.)

LET'S PRACTICE

Write five letters of the Greek alphabet in order.

Look at the Greek letter in the corner of each box. Find that letter in the words and circle it.

α	ἀγάπην ἀνήρ ἄλλαι
β	βάτου βόσκω βίβλου
γ	γέγοναν γίνομαι γράφω
δ	διδάσκω δίδωμι διώκω

☐ I practiced my flashcards today.

LET'S PRACTICE

Color the boxes orange if the letters match the letter in the larger box at the beginning of each row.

α	β	α	α	α
	δ	α	γ	β
β	β	γ	β	β
	ε	β	α	γ
γ	γ	γ	δ	α
	β	α	γ	γ
δ	δ	ε	δ	δ
	α	δ	δ	γ
ε	α	ε	ε	δ
	β	ε	δ	ε

☐ I practiced my flashcards today.

ZETA

Write the letter *zeta* across cach line.
As you write it, say "**zay**-ta."

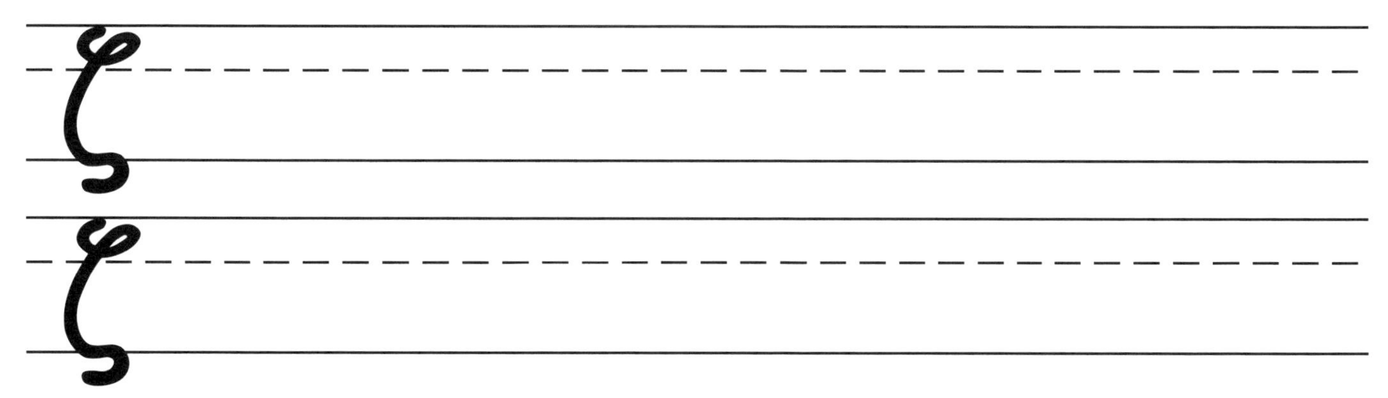

More Practice
with
ZETA

Zeta sounds like **dz** in ***adze***.

ζ

ζ

ζ

ζ

ζ

ζ

☐ I practiced my flashcards today.
(Remember to add this new card to your flashcards.)

LET'S PRACTICE

Write six letters of the Greek alphabet in order.

Write the names of the Greek letters.

α ________________

β ________________

γ ________________

δ ________________

ε ________________

ζ ________________

☐ I practiced my flashcards today.

LET'S PRACTICE

Look at the boxes. Circle the Greek letters that are the same in each box.

α β γ α	ζ β ε β	γ γ δ α	β δ δ ε
δ ζ ε ε	ζ β ζ δ	δ δ γ ζ	α ε β β
δ α α ε	γ ε α γ	β ε ε ζ	ζ ζ γ α
ε ε ζ γ	α δ α ε	δ α γ δ	ζ β β α

☐ I practiced my flashcards today.

ETA

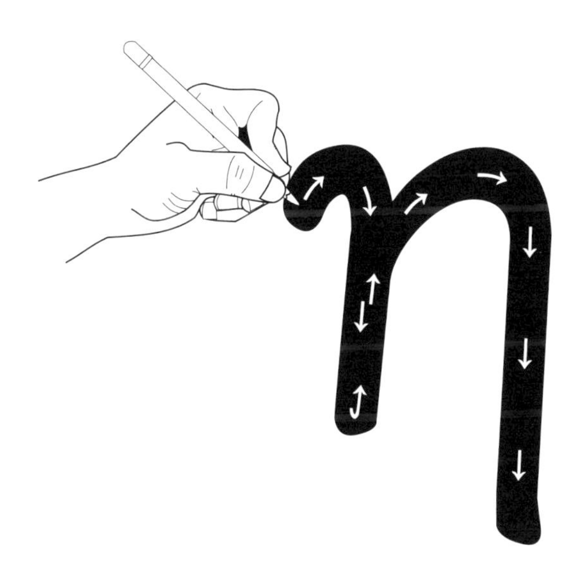

Write the letter *eta* across each line.
As you write it, say "**ay**-ta."

η

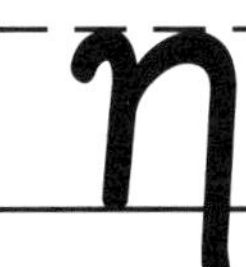

More Practice with ETA

Eta sounds like **a** in ***late***.

η

η

η

η

η

η

☐ I practiced my flashcards today.
(Remember to add this new card to your flashcards.)

LET'S PRACTICE

Write seven letters of the Greek alphabet in order.

Circle the name of the Greek letter at the beginning of each row.

δ	delta	beta	epsilon
η	zeta	gamma	eta
α	eta	alpha	gamma
ε	eta	epsilon	zeta
β	alpha	delta	beta
ζ	zeta	delta	alpha
γ	beta	gamma	epsilon

☐ I practiced my flashcards today.

LET'S PRACTICE

Color the triangle if the letter name matches the Greek letter at the top.

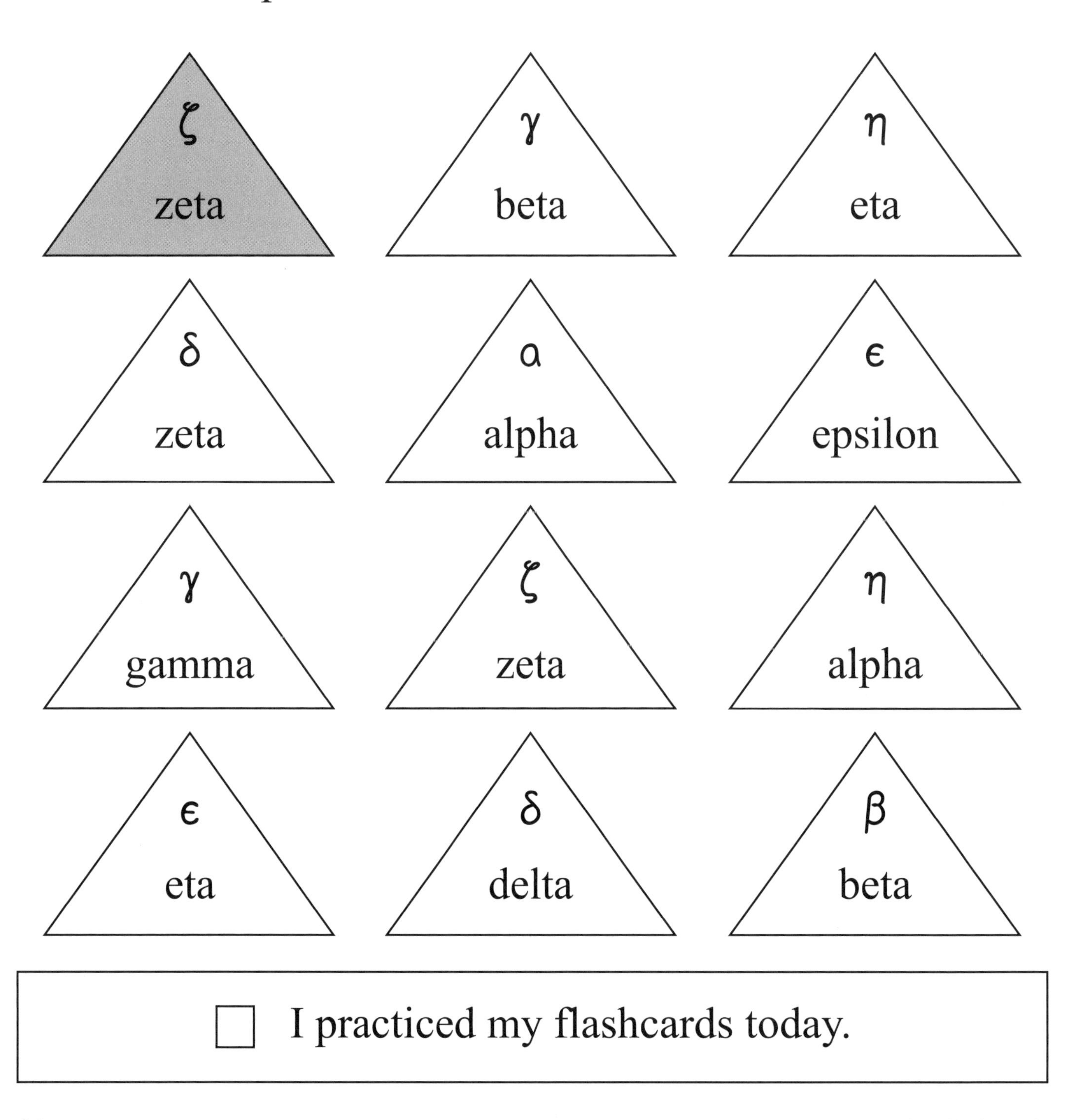

THETA

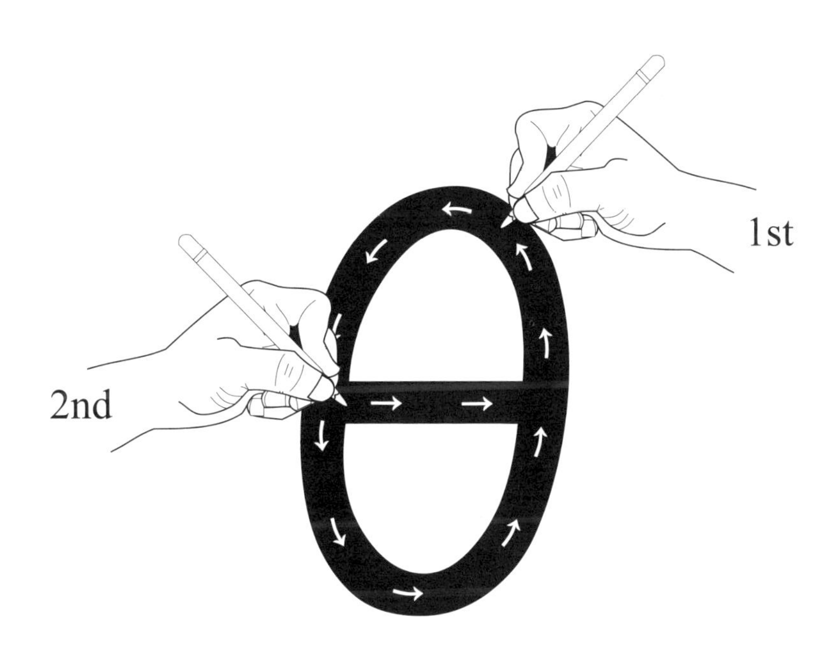

Write the letter *theta* across each line.
As you write it, say "**thay**-ta."

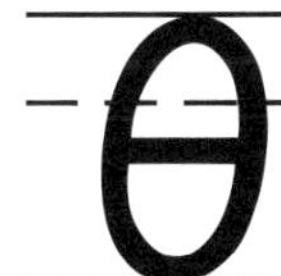

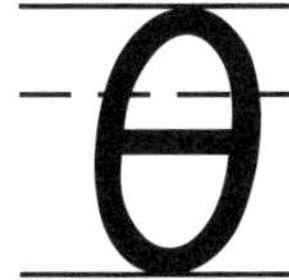

More Practice with THETA

Theta sounds like **th** in ***bath***.

θ

θ

θ

θ

θ

θ

☐ I practiced my flashcards today.
(Remember to add this new card to your flashcards.)

LET'S PRACTICE

Write eight letters of the Greek alphabet in order.

Read the letter names in the big boxes. Circle all the Greek letters that belong to each name.

gamma	β	ε	α	γ	γ	ε	γ	δ	δ
epsilon	ε	η	η	ε	ζ	η	α	θ	ε
eta	θ	η	ε	α	ε	ε	η	ζ	η
beta	γ	α	β	γ	β	η	δ	β	γ
zeta	ζ	δ	ε	δ	α	ζ	δ	ε	ζ
theta	γ	β	θ	θ	δ	β	θ	γ	β
delta	α	δ	ζ	β	δ	ζ	ζ	δ	β

☐ I practiced my flashcards today.

LET'S PRACTICE

Draw stems on the flowers to put them in their own vases.

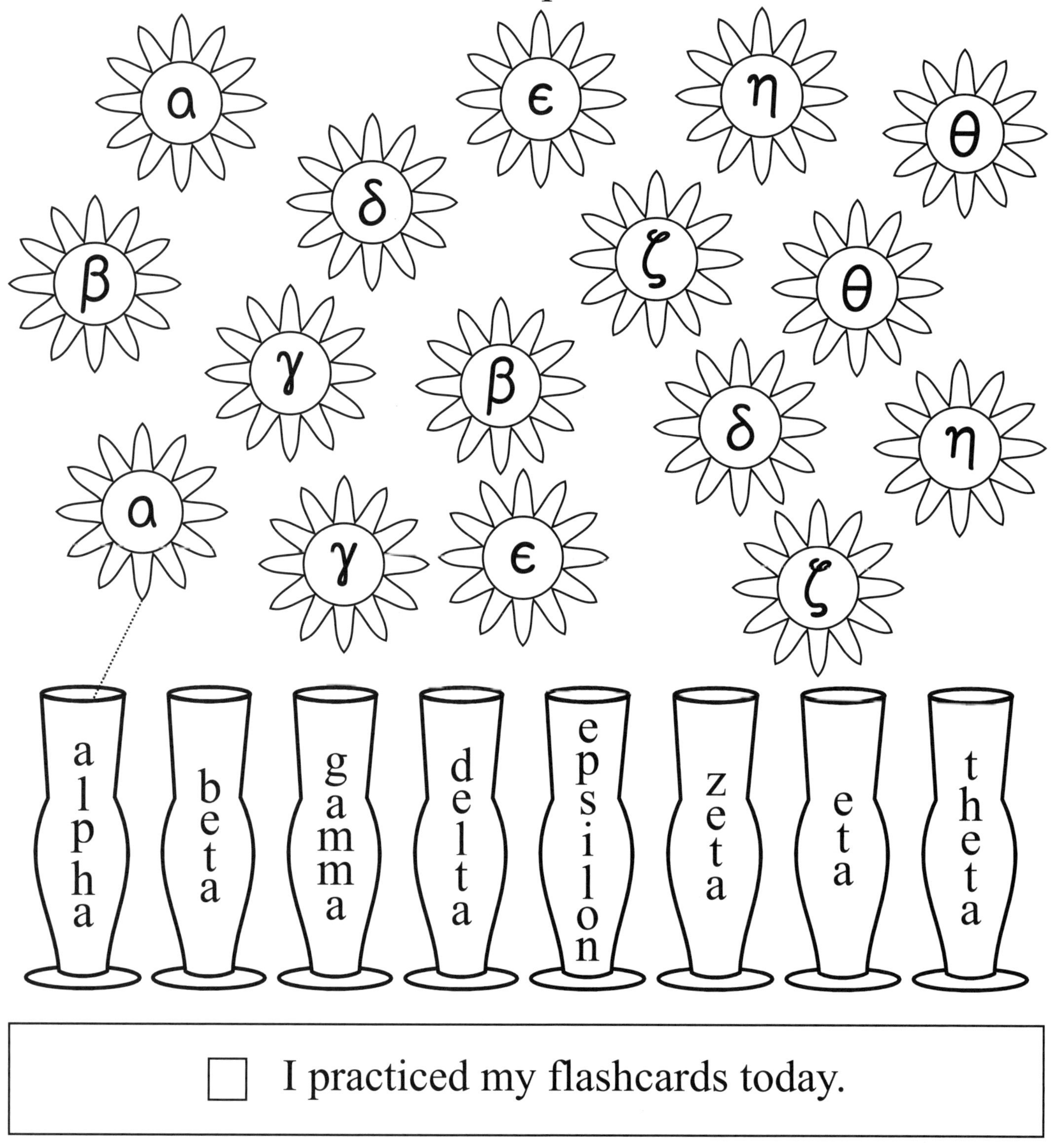

☐ I practiced my flashcards today.

IOTA

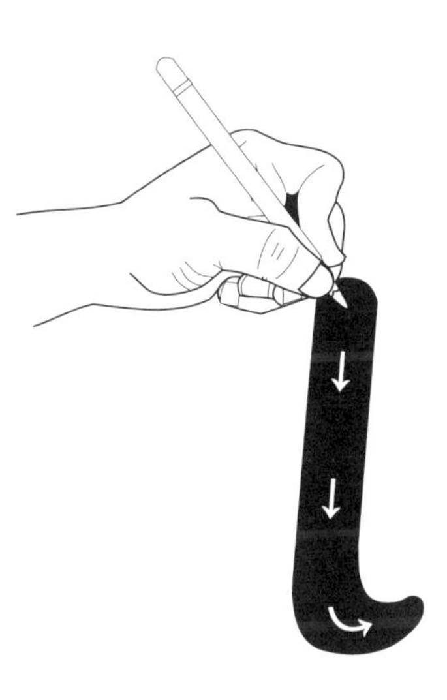

Write the letter *iota* across each line.
As you write it, say "ee-**o**-ta."

ι

ι

More Practice
with
IOTA

Iota sounds like **i** in ***pit***.

ι

ι

ι

ι

ι

ι

☐ I practiced my flashcards today.
(Remember to add this new card to your flashcards.)

LET'S PRACTICE

Write nine letters of the Greek alphabet in order.

Circle the correct letter names below the Greek letters.

θ		ϵ		β	
eta	theta	epsilon	delta	zeta	beta
δ		α		η	
delta	iota	theta	alpha	beta	eta
ζ		ι		γ	
gamma	zeta	iota	alpha	gamma	epsilon

☐ I practiced my flashcards today.

LET'S PRACTICE

Circle the words that have the same sound as the Greek letter at the beginning of each row.

δ	date	tent	blue
	sun	dog	bus
ι	miss	tool	rag
	coat	pray	bin
η	home	risk	cape
	pipe	same	stem
γ	sack	good	way
	Greek	rain	tug
θ	open	queen	math
	orange	bath	quit
ζ	adze	odds	fish
	dog	fork	bend
ϵ	cat	shoe	red
	wet	mice	yam

☐ I practiced my flashcards today.

KAPPA

Write the letter *kappa* across each line.
As you write it, say "**kap**-pa."

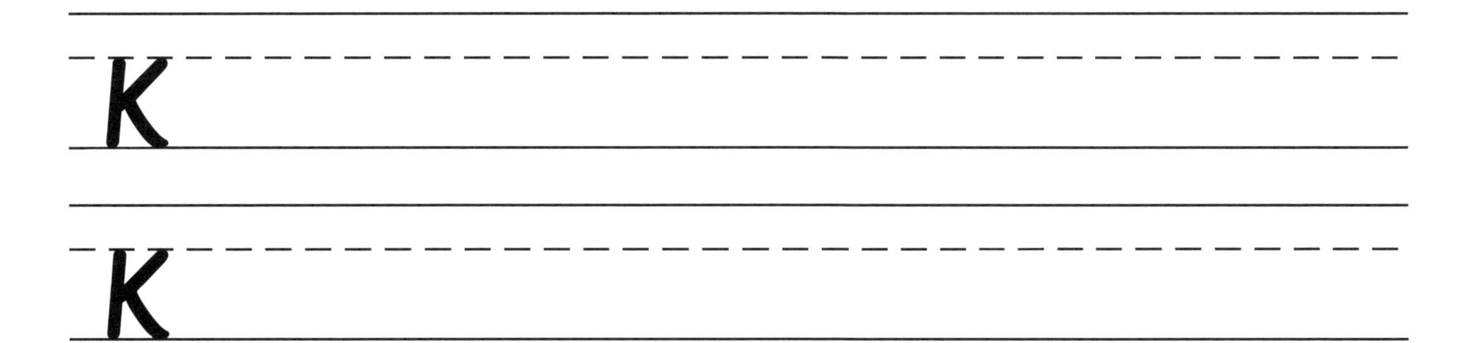

More Practice with KAPPA

Kappa sounds like **k** in ***kite***.

Κ

Κ

Κ

Κ

Κ

Κ

☐ I practiced my flashcards today.
(Remember to add this new card to your flashcards.)

LET'S PRACTICE

Write ten letters of the Greek alphabet in order.

Look at the Greek letter at the top of each box. Find that letter in the words below and circle it.

ι	δ	ζ	κ
ἰδίων βιβλίον ἰσχύν	δέω δίδωμι δολόω	ζόφον ζώνη ζήλου	καθότι κέκληκε κόκκον

θ	ε	γ	η
θέσθε θηρίον θύρα	ἔχω ἑτέρου εὑρέθη	γογγύζω γραφή γυνή	ἠνοίγη ἤχθη ἥκω

☐ I practiced my flashcards today.

LET'S PRACTICE

Tick-Tack-Toe!
Draw lines through three Greek letters that are alike.

δ δ ζ ζ ζ ζ ι κ ι	η η η β γ γ δ ζ η	θ ζ κ ι ι α δ δ δ	β α γ ε ε ε γ δ η
θ θ θ γ β ε δ ε γ	δ ζ δ κ κ κ ζ ε κ	ι κ β γ γ γ ζ α κ	ζ ζ ζ β γ ζ θ ι κ
δ δ δ ε ι ε γ β γ	γ δ ε α α α θ θ ι	η η η δ θ θ ε ι ε	β ε η α δ δ κ κ κ
ε ε ε α γ η θ ι κ	κ ε ι ι ι ι ζ θ ζ	ζ δ ζ θ θ θ α ε α	κ γ δ α κ α β β β

☐ I practiced my flashcards today.

LAMBDA

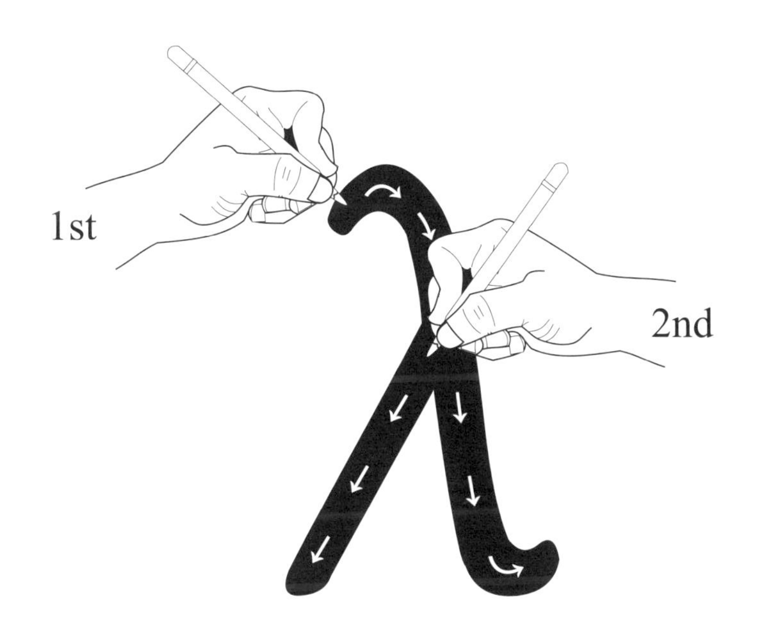

Write the letter *lambda* across each line.
As you write it, say "**lamb**-da."

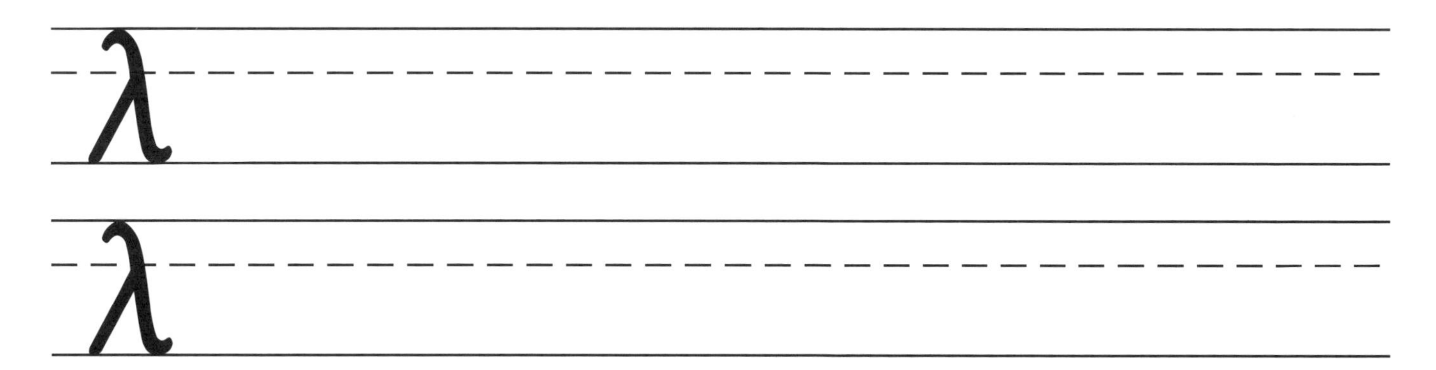

More Practice with LAMBDA

Lambda sounds like **l** in ***lamb***.

λ

λ

λ

λ

λ

λ

☐ I practiced my flashcards today.
(Remember to add this new card to your flashcards.)

LET'S PRACTICE

Write eleven letters of the Greek alphabet in order.

Look at the circled letter in each box. Which Greek letter comes next? Circle it.

Circled	Choices	Circled	Choices	Circled	Choices	Circled	Choices	Circled	Choices
η	λ	δ	ι	ζ	η	κ	ζ	β	γ
	δ		ε		γ		λ		ε
	θ		ζ		β		ι		κ
θ	ι	ι	κ	α	δ	ε	ζ	γ	η
	λ		β		θ		θ		δ
	ε		η		β		γ		κ

☐ I practiced my flashcards today.

LET'S PRACTICE

Circle the correct names of the Greek letters.

beta epsilon θ lambda theta	alpha eta ε epsilon zeta	theta alpha β kappa beta
eta delta κ kappa lambda	lambda gamma λ alpha zeta	iota eta η gamma epsilon
lambda delta δ beta zeta	gamma delta γ kappa theta	epsilon lambda ι iota alpha
theta alpha α gamma kappa	delta beta ζ iota zeta	lambda delta λ iota gamma

☐ I practiced my flashcards today.

MU

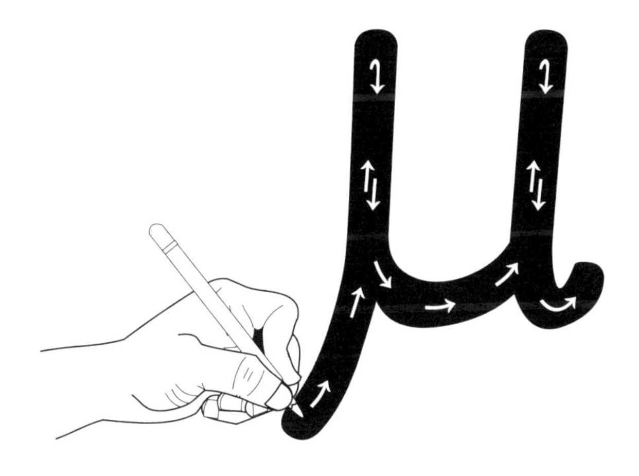

Write the letter *mu* across each line.
As you write it, say "**moo.**"

μ

More Practice with MU

Mu sounds like **m** in ***man***.

μ

μ

μ

μ

μ

μ

☐ I practiced my flashcards today.
(Remember to add this new card to your flashcards.)

LET'S PRACTICE

Write twelve letters of the Greek alphabet in order.

Draw lines from the Greek letters to their names.

ε	theta	η	iota
γ	epsilon	β	lambda
α	mu	ι	eta
κ	alpha	λ	beta
μ	kappa	δ	zeta
θ	gamma	ζ	delta

☐ I practiced my flashcards today.

LET'S PRACTICE

Write the correct Greek letters on the lines.

gamma ______ kappa ______ zeta ______

alpha ______ iota ______ epsilon ______

mu ______ theta ______ delta ______

lambda ______ eta ______ beta ______

Which letters go below the line?

______ ______ ______ ______ ______

Which letters are tall?

______ ______ ______ ______ ______

☐ I practiced my flashcards today.

NU

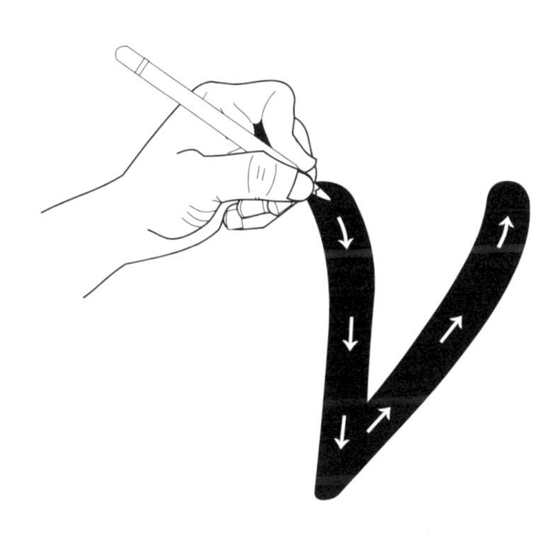

Write the letter *nu* across each line.
As you write it, say "**noo**."

ν

ν

More Practice
with
NU

Nu sounds like **n** in ***nice***.

ν

ν

ν

ν

ν

ν

☐ I practiced my flashcards today.
(Remember to add this new card to your flashcards.)

LET'S PRACTICE

Write thirteen letters of the Greek alphabet in order.

Connect the dots in the correct order.

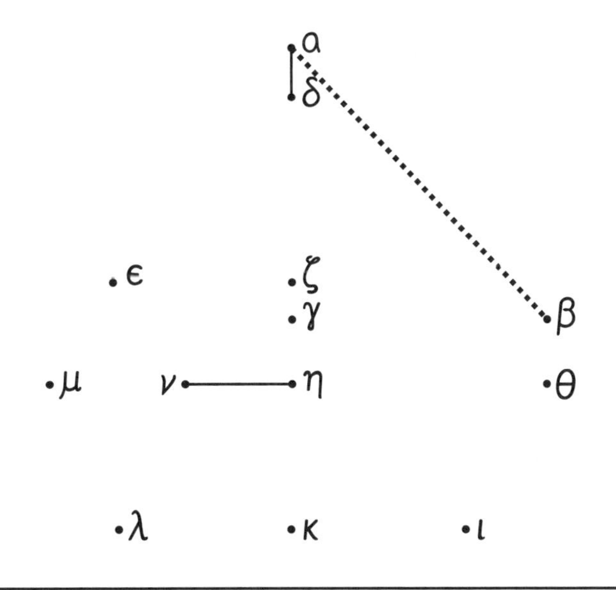

☐ I practiced my flashcards today.

LET'S PRACTICE

Circle the correct Greek letters.

lambda	θ	λ	α
eta	η	ε	ζ
theta	γ	δ	θ
kappa	η	ι	κ
mu	μ	β	λ
delta	ζ	δ	α
iota	ν	ι	β
epsilon	ε	η	ι
nu	κ	μ	ν
zeta	θ	ζ	γ
gamma	γ	κ	δ

☐ I practiced my flashcards today.

XI

Write the letter *xi* across each line.
As you write it, say "**ksee**."

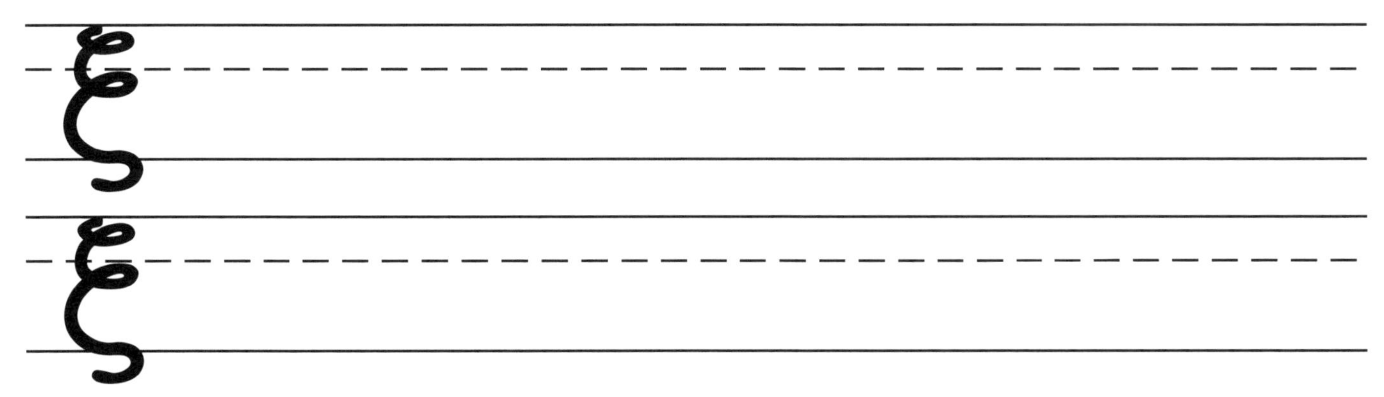

More Practice
with
XI

Xi sounds like **x** in ***box***.

ξ

ξ

ξ

ξ

ξ

ξ

☐ I practiced my flashcards today.
(Remember to add this new card to your flashcards.)

LET'S PRACTICE

Write fourteen letters of the Greek alphabet in order.

Circle all the Greek letters you have learned so far.

ι f j θ m g κ

η δ Q μ γ z

h ν

ξ λ B

β c α R ζ ϵ

☐ I practiced my flashcards today.

LET'S PRACTICE

Circle the correct names of the Greek letters.

β	beta kappa zeta	κ	alpha eta kappa	η	nu eta epsilon
λ	delta gamma lambda	ν	gamma nu lambda	ϵ	mu iota epsilon
μ	delta mu gamma	θ	gamma theta beta	ξ	lambda xi delta
ζ	beta xi zeta	ι	epsilon iota lambda	δ	delta theta kappa

☐ I practiced my flashcards today.

OMICRON

Write the letter *omicron* across each line.
As you write it, say "**ahm**-i-cron."

More Practice with OMICRON

Omicron sounds like **o** in ***obey***.

ο

ο

ο

ο

ο

ο

☐ I practiced my flashcards today.
(Remember to add this new card to your flashcards.)

LET'S PRACTICE

Write fifteen letters of the Greek alphabet in order.

Circle the Greek letters that are the same in each box.

κ α γ κ	η λ λ ν	ο δ ο α	ξ ξ μ ε
ι μ λ μ	θ β ζ θ	ι κ γ ι	α θ ν ν

☐ I practiced my flashcards today.

LET'S PRACTICE

Circle the correct letter names below the Greek letters.

ν		ξ		β	
kappa	nu	xi	nu	omicron	beta
κ		α		μ	
theta	kappa	alpha	delta	mu	lambda
λ		ο		γ	
iota	lambda	omicron	mu	gamma	xi
ι		ε		δ	
eta	iota	epsilon	alpha	beta	delta
θ		η		ζ	
zeta	theta	eta	epsilon	zeta	gamma

☐ I practiced my flashcards today.

PI

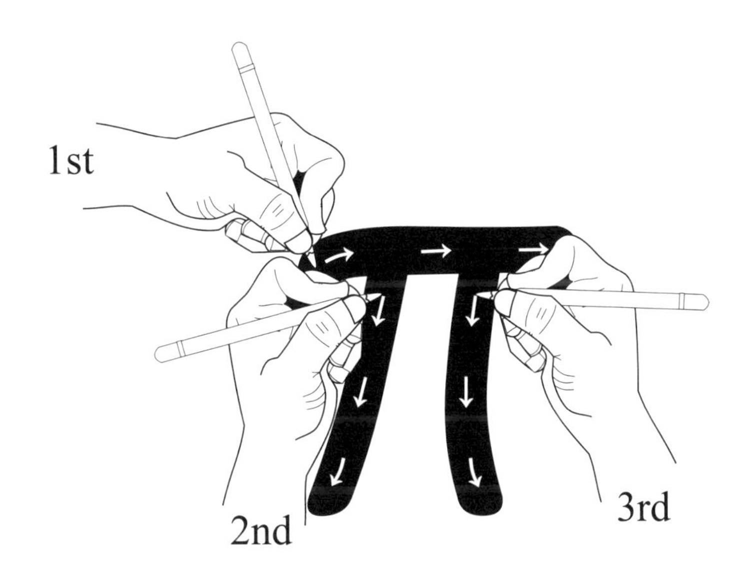

Write the letter *pi* across each line.
As you write it, say "**pie**."

π

π

More Practice
with
PI

Pi sounds like **p** in ***pie***.

π

π

π

π

π

π

☐ I practiced my flashcards today.
(Remember to add this new card to your flashcards.)

LET'S PRACTICE

Write sixteen letters of the Greek alphabet in order.

Read the letter names in the big boxes. Circle all the Greek letters that belong to each name.

pi	η	π	η	π	μ	π	π	ν	μ
omicron	ο	λ	ο	ο	θ	θ	ο	λ	θ
xi	ξ	ξ	κ	ξ	λ	ξ	κ	κ	λ

☐ I practiced my flashcards today.

LET'S PRACTICE

Draw lines from the Greek letters to their sounds.

κ	**p** in ***pie***	β	**a** in ***late***
δ	**a** in ***father***	ν	**o** in ***obey***
π	**d** in ***dog***	η	**b** in ***bat***
α	**k** in ***kite***	ο	**n** in ***nice***
λ	**th** in ***bath***	ϵ	**e** in ***get***
θ	**l** in ***lamb***	μ	**i** in ***pit***
ξ	**dz** in ***adze***	ι	**m** in ***man***
ζ	**x** in ***box***	γ	**g** in ***God***

☐ I practiced my flashcards today.

RHO

Write the letter *rho* across each line.
As you write it, say "**row**."

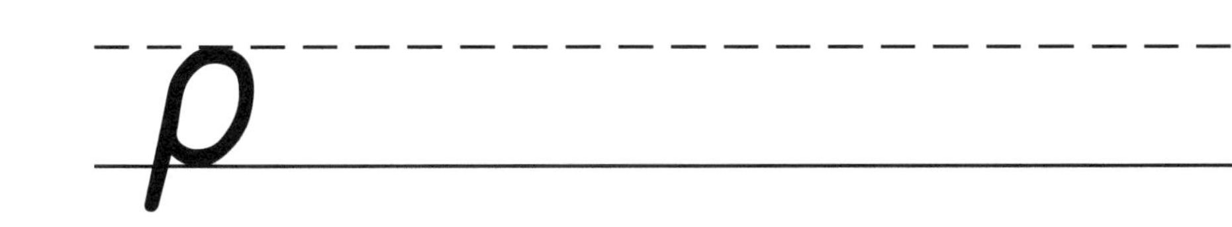

More Practice with RHO

Rho sounds like **r** in ***row***.

ρ

ρ

ρ

ρ

ρ

ρ

☐ I practiced my flashcards today.
(Remember to add this new card to your flashcards.)

LET'S PRACTICE

Write seventeen letters of the Greek alphabet in order.

What's my sound? Draw lines from the letters to the words that have that sound.

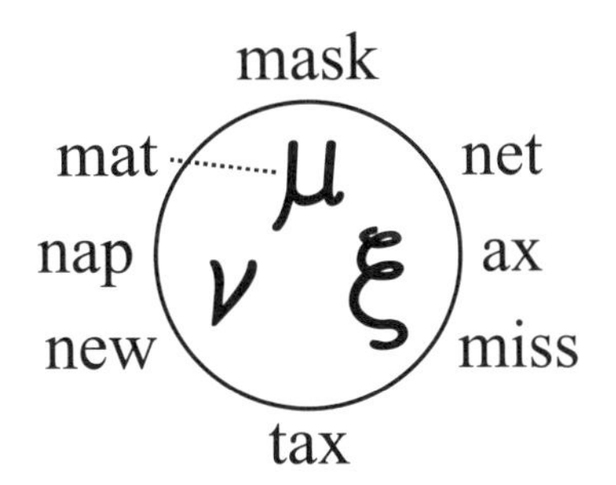

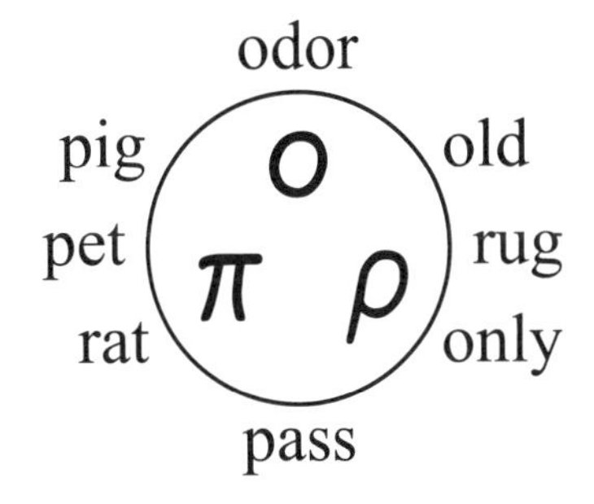

☐ I practiced my flashcards today.

LET'S PRACTICE

Write the names of the Greek letters.

α	______________	κ	______________
β	______________	λ	______________
γ	______________	μ	______________
δ	______________	ν	______________
ε	______________	ξ	______________
ζ	______________	ο	______________
η	______________	π	______________
θ	______________	ρ	______________
ι	______________		

☐ I practiced my flashcards today.

SIGMA

(Both sigmas have the same sound.
The σ is used at the beginning or
middle of a word; the ς at the end.)

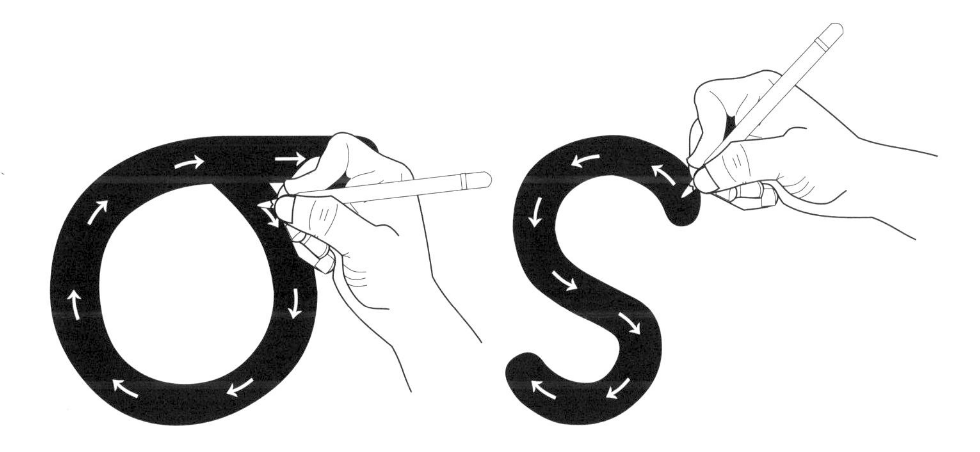

Write the letter *sigma* across each line.
As you write it, say "**sig**-ma."

More Practice with SIGMA

Sigma sounds like **s** in ***sit***.

σ

s

σ

s

σ

s

☐ I practiced my flashcards today.
(Remember to add these new cards to your flashcards.)

LET'S PRACTICE

Write eighteen letters of the Greek alphabet in order.

Connect the dots.

λ κ μ ι ν θ ξ γ δ α β ε ζ η ο ρ σ π

☐ I practiced my flashcards today.

LET'S PRACTICE

Draw lines from the Greek letters to their names.

ζ	rho	γ	delta
ο	zeta	δ	gamma
σ	pi	κ	alpha
ρ	omicron	ι	iota
π	sigma	α	kappa
λ	xi	θ	eta
ν	lambda	η	epsilon
μ	nu	β	theta
ξ	mu	ϵ	beta

☐ I practiced my flashcards today.

TAU

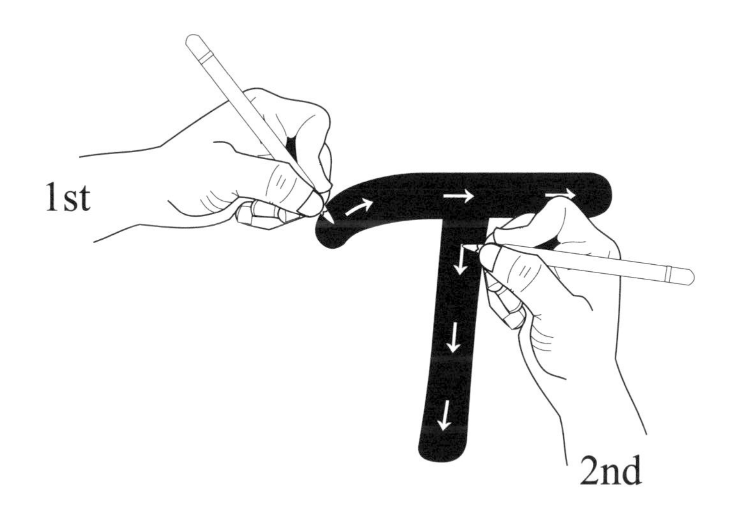

Write the letter *tau* across each line.
As you write it, say "**tou**."

More Practice with TAU

Tau sounds like **t** in ***toy***.

τ

τ

τ

τ

τ

τ

☐ I practiced my flashcards today.
(Remember to add this new card to your flashcards.)

LET'S PRACTICE

Write nineteen letters of the Greek alphabet in order.

Look at the Greek letter at the top of each box. Find that letter in the words below and circle it.

π	ρ	σ	τ
πέπωκε πέριξ πέντε	ῥίπτω ῥήγνυμι ῥαντίζω	σινδών σκηνήν στάσιν	τρίτη τίκτω ταῦτα

☐ I practiced my flashcards today.

LET'S PRACTICE

Draw circles around the Greek letters and their names.

τ pi π tau	α alpha nu ν	zeta gamma ζ γ	iota ι ο omicron
σ ρ sigma rho	eta λ lambda η	μ mu ν nu	κ theta kappa θ
epsilon theta θ ϵ	beta ξ β xi	ρ π pi rho	eta η delta δ
λ iota ι lambda	ο omicron sigma σ	kappa xi κ ξ	mu μ τ tau

☐ I practiced my flashcards today.

UPSILON

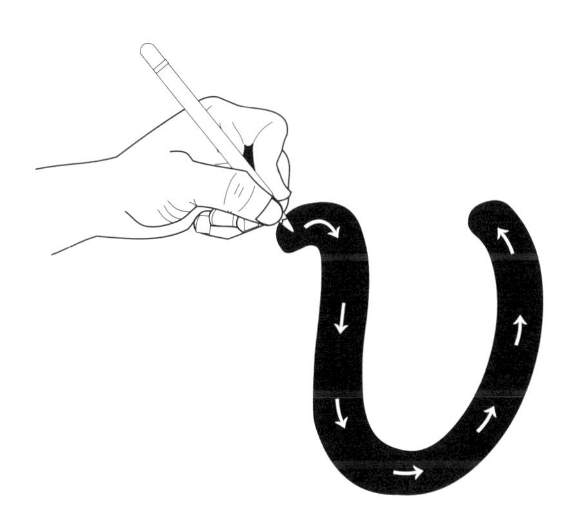

Write the letter *upsilon* across each line.
As you write it, say "**up**-si-lon."

υ

υ

More Practice
with
UPSILON

Upsilon sounds like **oo** in ***good***.

υ

υ

υ

υ

υ

υ

☐ I practiced my flashcards today.
(Remember to add this new card to your flashcards.)

LET'S PRACTICE

Write twenty letters of the Greek alphabet in order.

Color the boxes orange if the letters match the letter in the larger box at the beginning of each row.

τ	π	λ	κ	τ	κ	π	τ	μ	τ	λ
	τ	π	μ	λ	π	μ	λ	π	τ	κ
υ	υ	γ	υ	ν	γ	υ	σ	η	ο	ν
	ν	η	υ	σ	ν	η	ο	υ	γ	η

☐ I practiced my flashcards today.

LET'S PRACTICE

Circle the name of the Greek letter at the beginning of each row.

ξ	alpha	mu	lambda	delta
	epsilon	zeta	xi	pi
σ	delta	sigma	eta	nu
	iota	gamma	omicron	theta
υ	zeta	rho	theta	upsilon
	epsilon	lambda	tau	sigma
π	iota	xi	beta	nu
	pi	zeta	mu	kappa
τ	kappa	tau	theta	iota
	alpha	sigma	eta	delta
ο	delta	gamma	theta	upsilon
	alpha	iota	mu	omicron
ρ	rho	beta	pi	delta
	tau	theta	gamma	lambda

☐ I practiced my flashcards today.

PHI

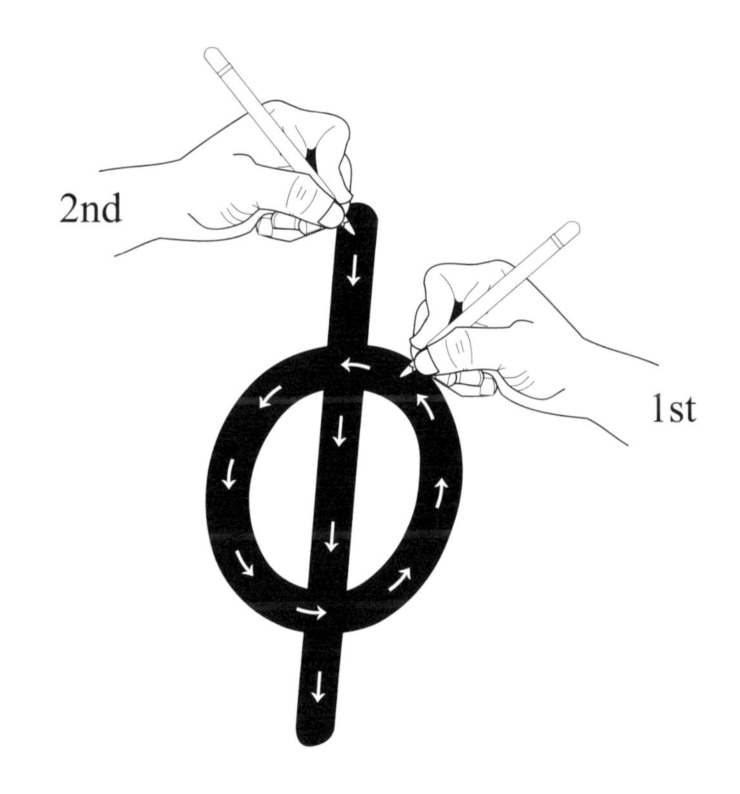

Write the letter *phi* across each line.
As you write it, say "**fee**."

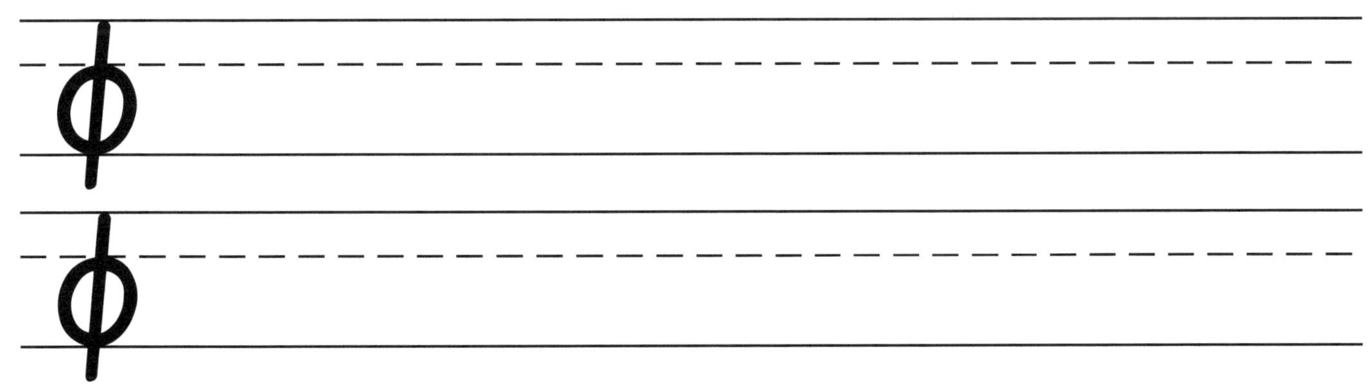

More Practice
with
PHI

Phi sounds like **f** in ***fun***.

ϕ

ϕ

ϕ

ϕ

ϕ

ϕ

☐ I practiced my flashcards today.
(Remember to add this new card to your flashcards.)

LET'S PRACTICE

Write twenty-one letters of the Greek alphabet in order.

Circle the words that have the Greek letter sound.

ϕ	fun	face	bug
	one	fish	game

☐ I practiced my flashcards today.

LET'S PRACTICE

Draw stems on the flowers to put them in their own vases.

☐ I practiced my flashcards today.

CHI

Write the letter *chi* across each line.
As you write it, say "**kee**."

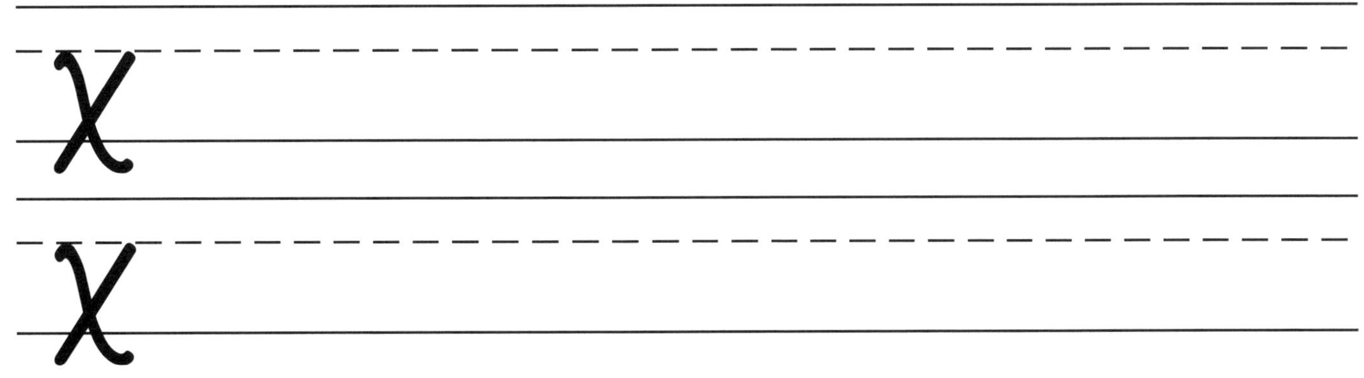

More Practice with CHI

Chi sounds like the German **ch** in ***Ach***.

χ

χ

χ

χ

χ

χ

☐ I practiced my flashcards today.
(Remember to add this new card to your flashcards.)

LET'S PRACTICE

Write twenty-two letters of the Greek alphabet in order.

Draw lines through three Greek letters that are alike.

χ χ χ	υ ο ο	π π τ	ξ ξ ξ
φ ρ φ	σ σ σ	τ τ τ	χ φ χ

☐ I practiced my flashcards today.

LET'S PRACTICE

Color the triangle if the letter name matches the Greek letter at the top.

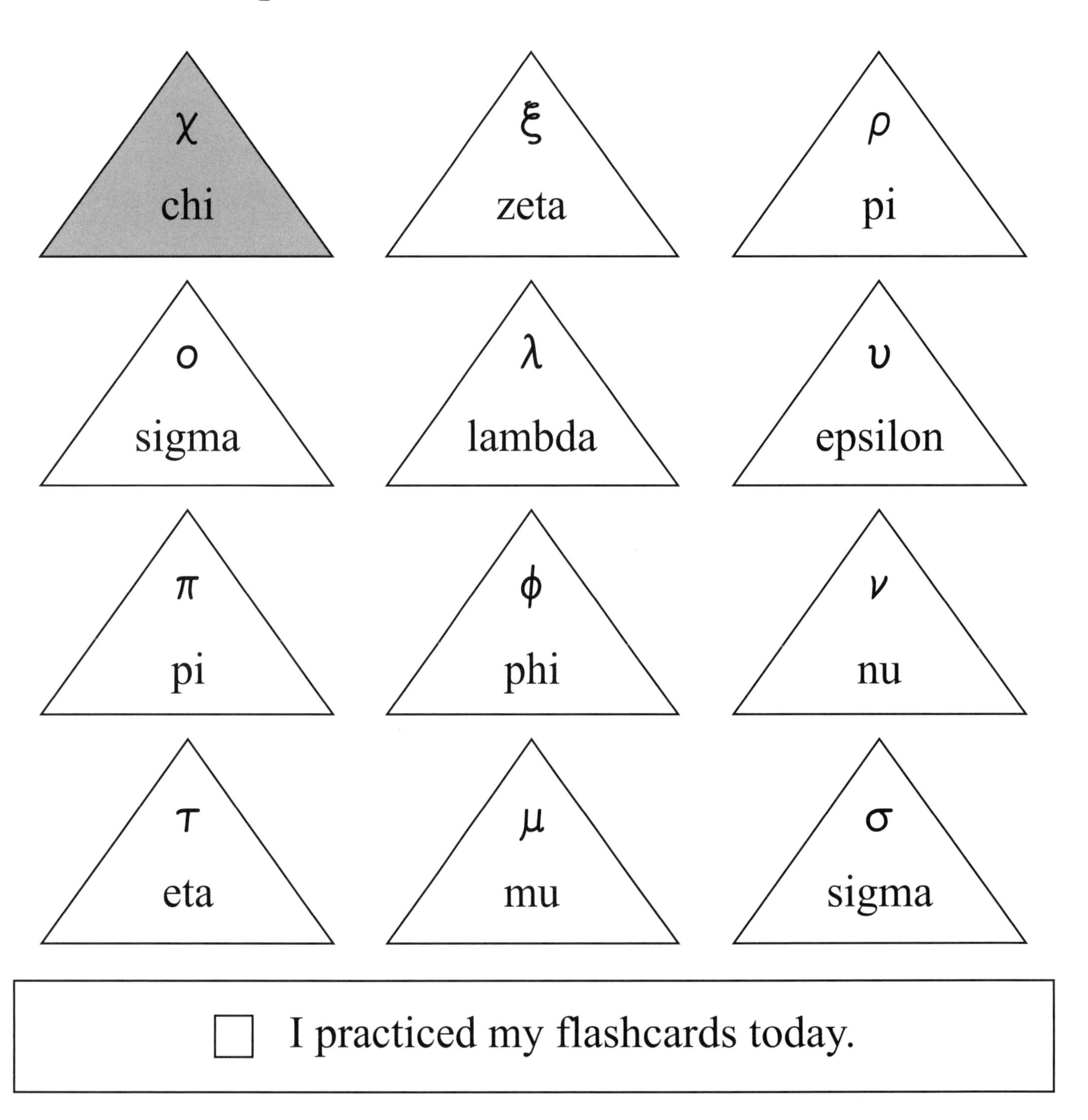

☐ I practiced my flashcards today.

PSI

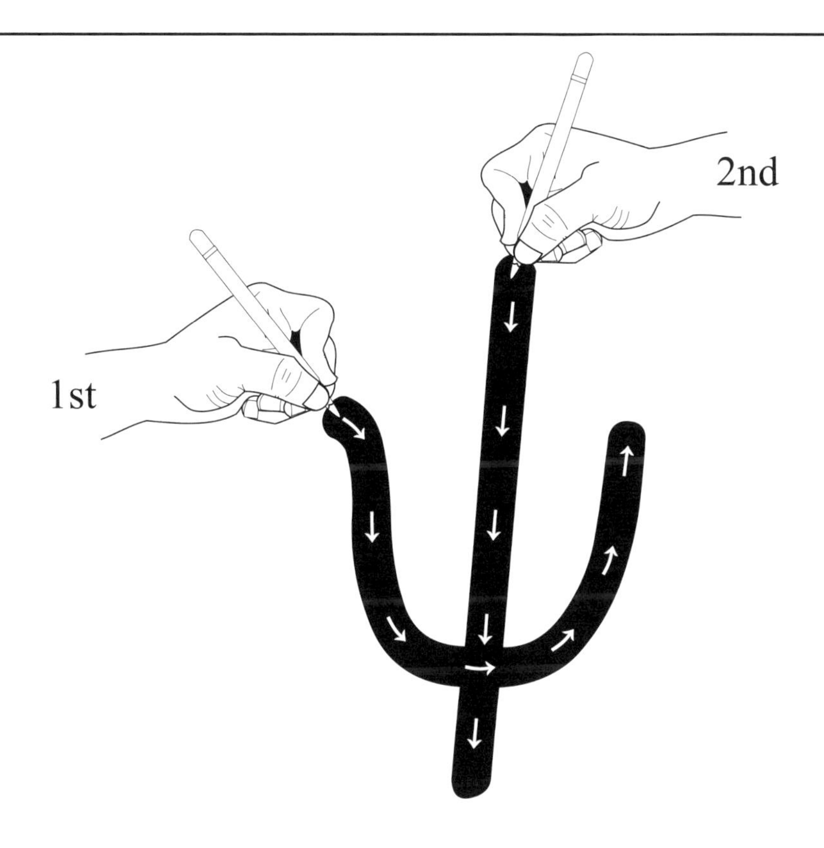

Write the letter *psi* across each line.
As you write it, say "**psee**."

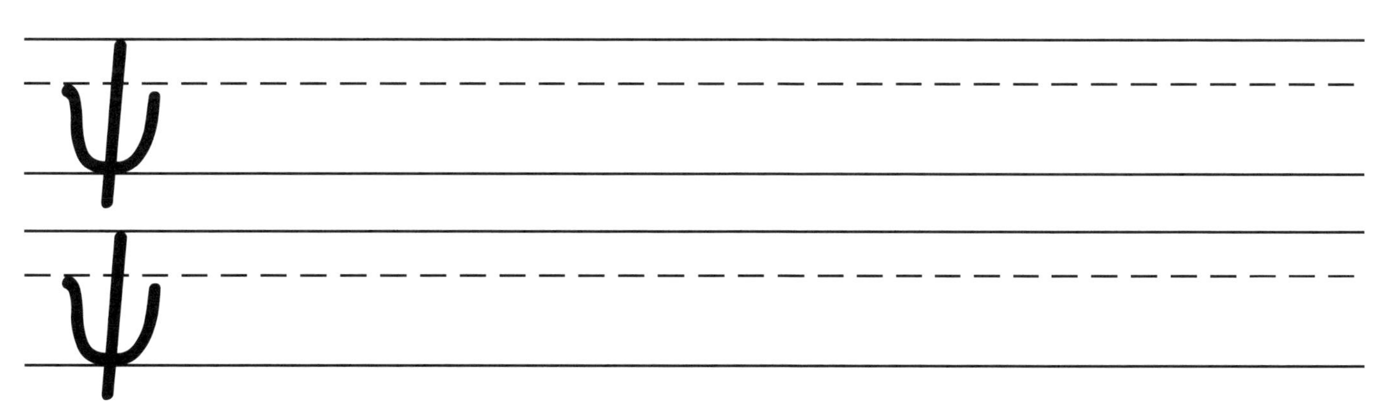

More Practice
with
PSI

Psi sounds like **ps** in ***lips***.

ψ

ψ

ψ

ψ

ψ

ψ

☐ I practiced my flashcards today.
(Remember to add this new card to your flashcards.)

LET'S PRACTICE

Write twenty-three letters of the Greek alphabet in order.

Look at the circled letter in each box. Which Greek letter comes next? Circle it.

Circled	Choices	Circled	Choices	Circled	Choices	Circled	Choices	Circled	Choices
χ	φ / ψ	τ	υ / π	φ	ψ / χ	ρ	σ / τ	υ	ο / φ

☐ I practiced my flashcards today.

LET'S PRACTICE

Blast the rockets to their moons.

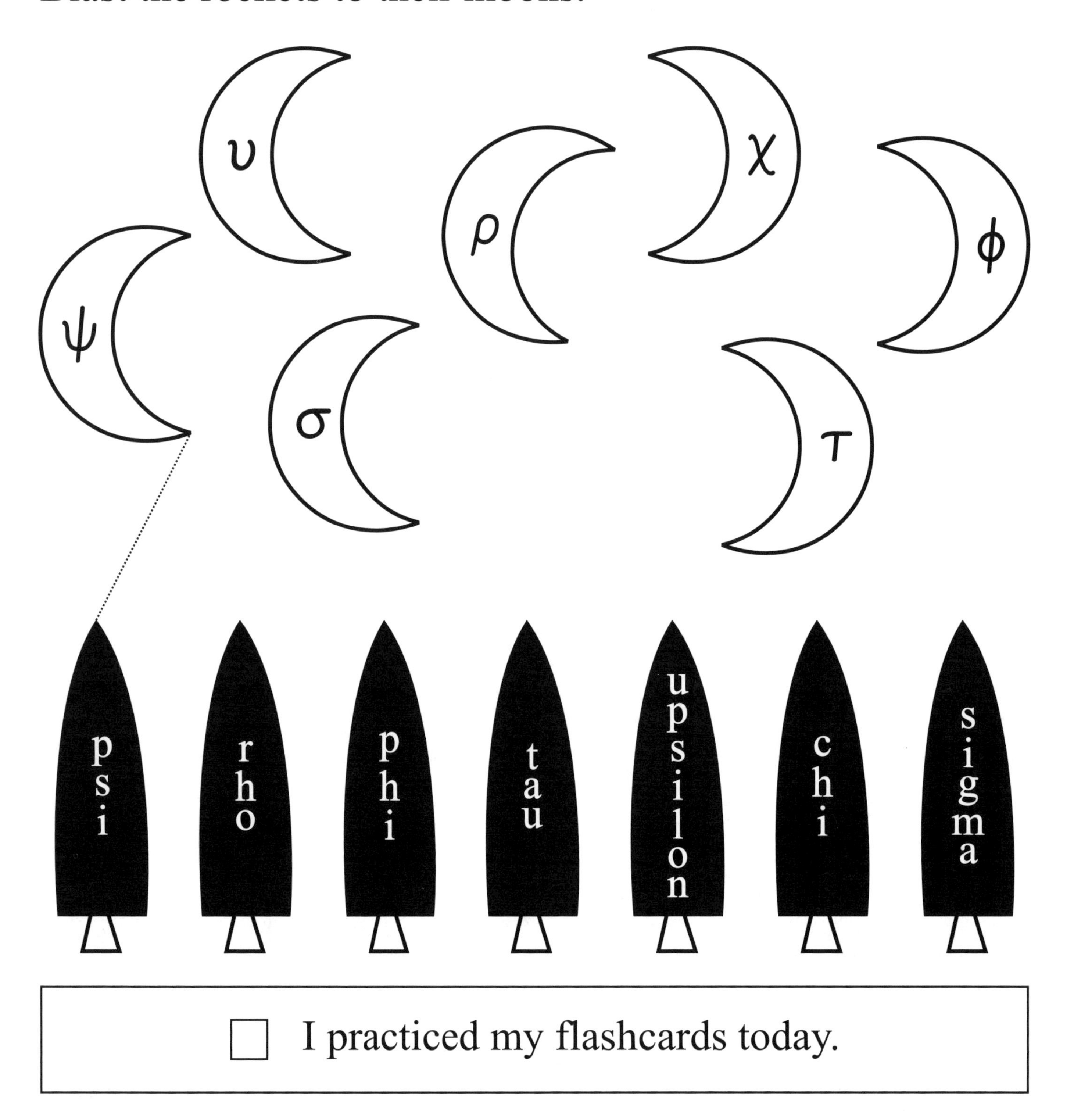

☐ I practiced my flashcards today.

OMEGA

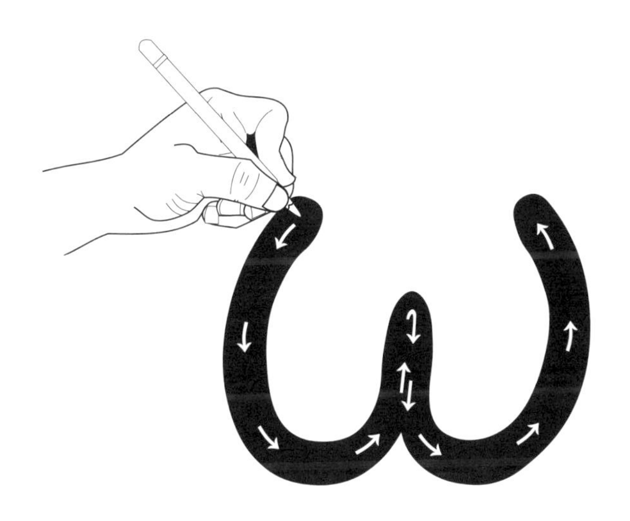

Write the letter *omega* across each line.
As you write it, say "o-**may**-ga."

More Practice
with
OMEGA

Omega sounds like **o** in ***note***.

ω

ω

ω

ω

ω

ω

☐ I practiced my flashcards today.
(Remember to add this new card to your flashcards.)

LET'S PRACTICE

Write twenty-four letters of the Greek alphabet in order.

Blacken the boxes with Greek letters to find a message.

τ	t	κ	ζ	h	π	ξ	i	ψ	s	χ	ι	i	s	γ	ν
λ	π	g	φ	ρ	r	δ	e	γ	a	α	ω	t	θ	ζ	σ
θ	G	β	υ	r	η	χ	e	λ	φ	e	μ	ε	k	ξ	ρ

☐ I practiced my flashcards today.

CHALLENGE!

Circle the names of the twenty-four Greek letters.

A	B	S	H	J	W	D	E	L	T	A	Z	R	P	Q	L	S	M
H	C	N	Z	X	R	G	P	Z	S	D	O	X	S	P	B	C	R
P	Q	D	J	K	Z	P	S	D	B	H	T	R	F	H	G	L	N
L	D	F	G	H	O	M	I	C	R	O	N	M	T	I	B	A	Z
A	C	H	J	B	G	C	L	R	Y	X	G	Y	H	S	C	M	U
K	T	P	M	V	N	W	O	M	Z	T	C	Q	N	G	H	B	J
T	R	O	S	Y	Z	B	N	U	C	D	F	P	G	K	M	D	L
B	L	C	I	G	J	F	P	Z	Y	V	S	K	A	P	P	A	R
M	P	K	L	D	N	S	H	W	T	Q	S	T	M	R	V	C	B
P	B	Z	Y	X	I	W	P	R	M	G	Y	Z	M	W	D	F	H
M	L	H	J	L	S	V	T	Q	J	N	S	L	A	T	E	Z	K
I	P	K	O	P	G	C	F	B	K	H	N	M	T	W	Z	B	F
R	C	N	Q	P	R	D	E	M	J	R	L	S	Q	P	V	D	C
T	X	W	T	S	D	T	B	V	L	R	K	N	J	G	P	S	I
S	T	H	E	T	A	C	F	G	S	I	G	M	A	H	M	G	H
F	B	G	P	A	V	K	S	M	W	S	G	T	Z	W	V	B	C
C	S	J	F	U	H	L	G	T	T	M	E	V	F	B	D	M	F
J	T	L	C	B	G	O	M	E	G	A	S	M	C	F	G	S	L

☐ I practiced my flashcards today.

κύριος

means

Lord

It sounds like **koo**-ree-os.

Write the Greek word that means **Lord** on the lines below. Say it as you write it.

☐ I practiced my flashcards today.
(Remember to add this new card to your flashcards.)

More Practice with κύριος

Write the Greek word for **Lord** on each fish.

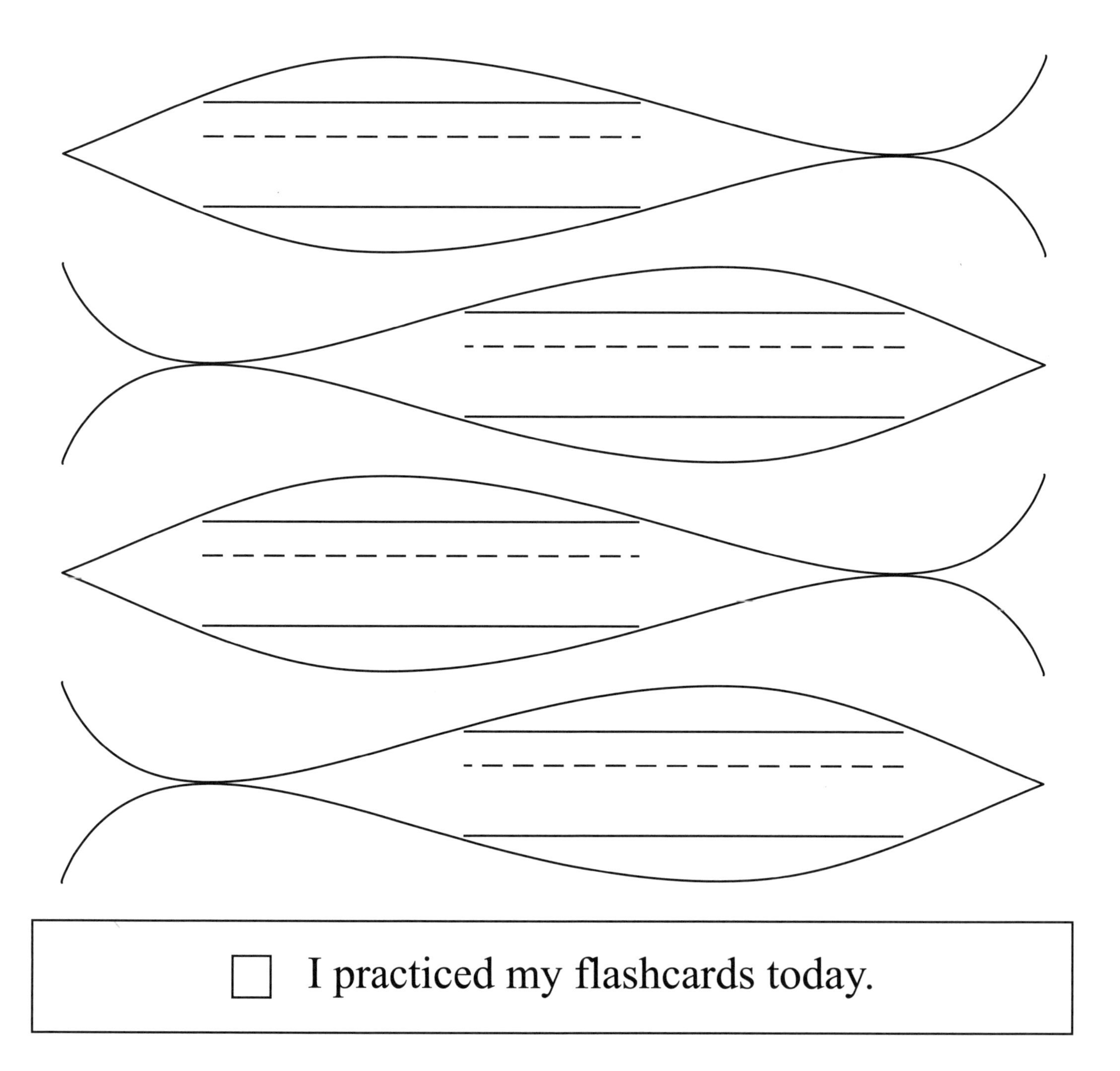

☐ I practiced my flashcards today.

ἐμοὶ

means

my

It sounds like e-**moy**.

Write the Greek word that means **my** on the lines below. Say it as you write it.

☐ I practiced my flashcards today.
(Remember to add this new card to your flashcards.)

More Practice
with
ἐμοὶ

Write the Greek word for **my** on each beach ball.

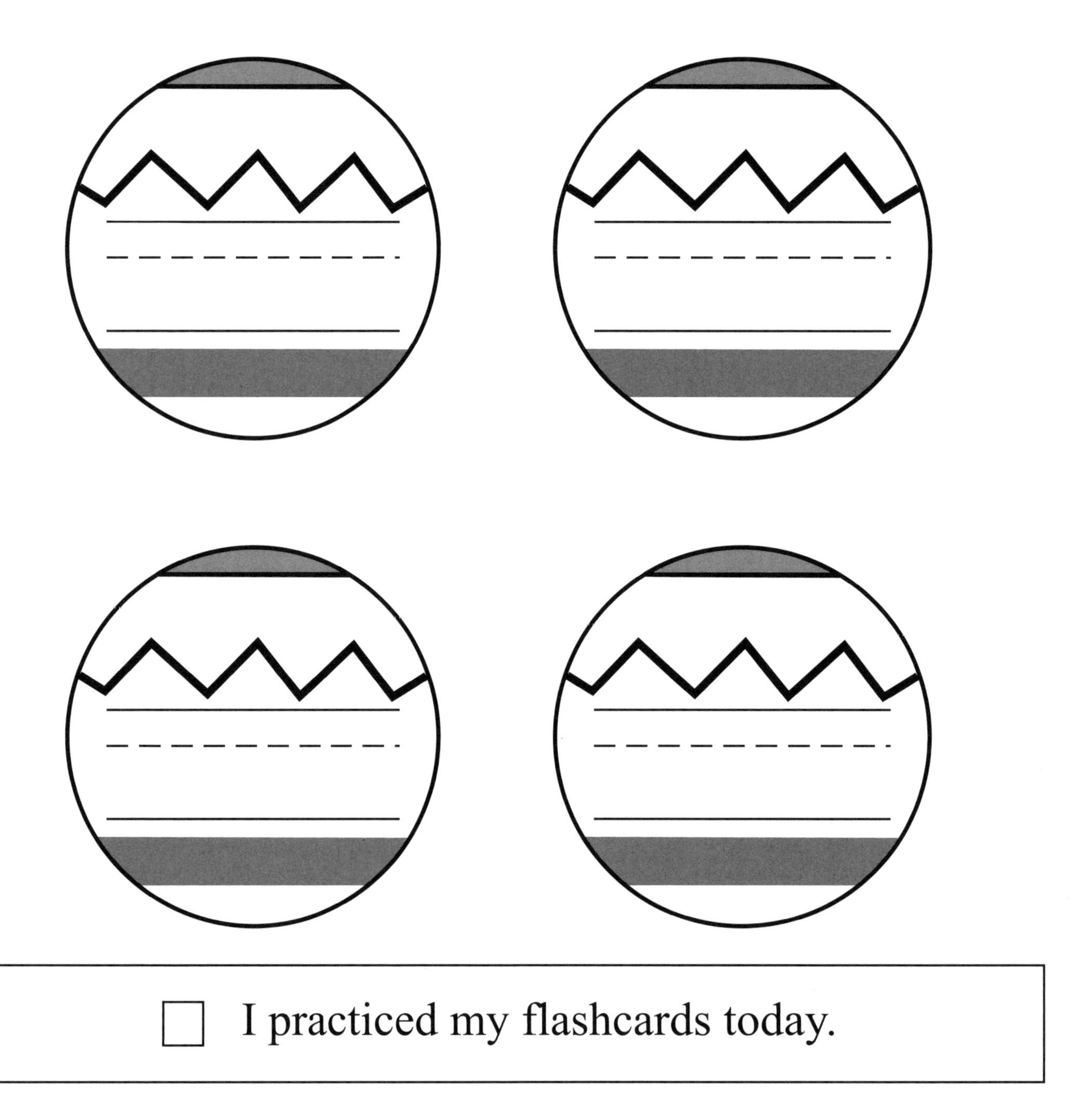

☐ I practiced my flashcards today.

LET'S PRACTICE

Draw lines from the words to their meanings.

κύριος	my
ἐμοὶ	Lord

Write the meanings of these words.

κύριος ______________

ἐμοὶ ______________

Circle all the words that mean the same as the first word in each row.

my	ἐμοὶ	ἐμοὶ	μύρον
	βλέπω	μέλι	ἐμοὶ
Lord	κύων	κύριος	κλίνω
	κύριος	κωφόν	κύριος

☐ I practiced my flashcards today.

LET'S PRACTICE

Put the apples on the correct tree.

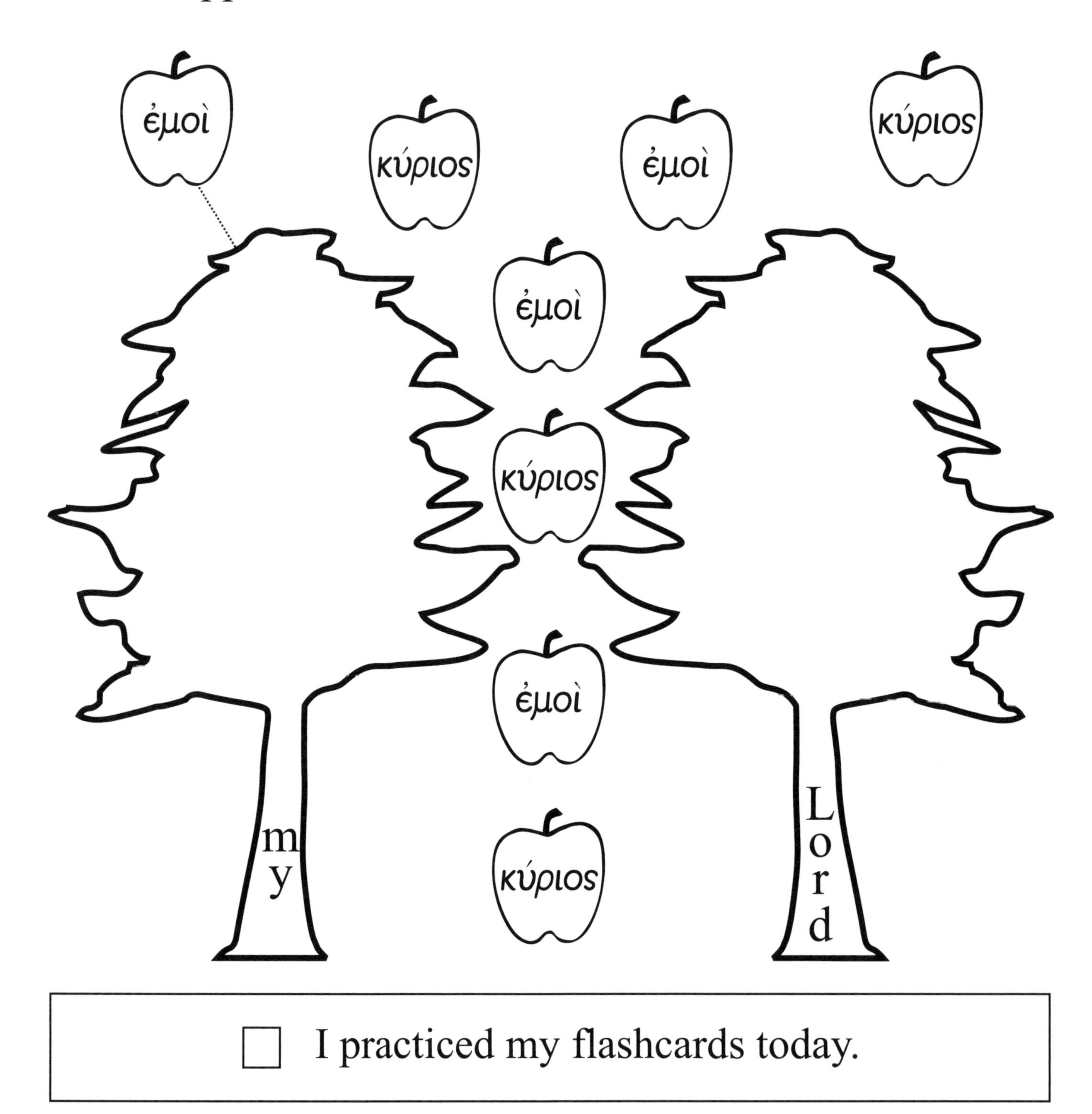

☐ I practiced my flashcards today.

βοηθός

means

helper

It sounds like bo-ay-**thos**.

Write the Greek word that means **helper** on the lines below. Say it as you write it.

☐ I practiced my flashcards today.
(Remember to add this new card to your flashcards.)

More Practice
with
βοηθός

Write the Greek word for **helper** on each watermelon.

☐ I practiced my flashcards today.

LET'S PRACTICE

Write the definition beneath each word.

ἐμοὶ βοηθός κύριος

____________ ____________ ____________

Circle all the words that mean the same as the first word in each row.

βοηθός	helper	helper	doctor
	teacher	helper	teacher
κύριος	nurse	Lord	Lord
	cross	nurse	cross
ἐμοὶ	my	his	his
	my	your	my

☐ I practiced my flashcards today.

LET'S PRACTICE

Draw lines from the balloons to the correct clown hats.

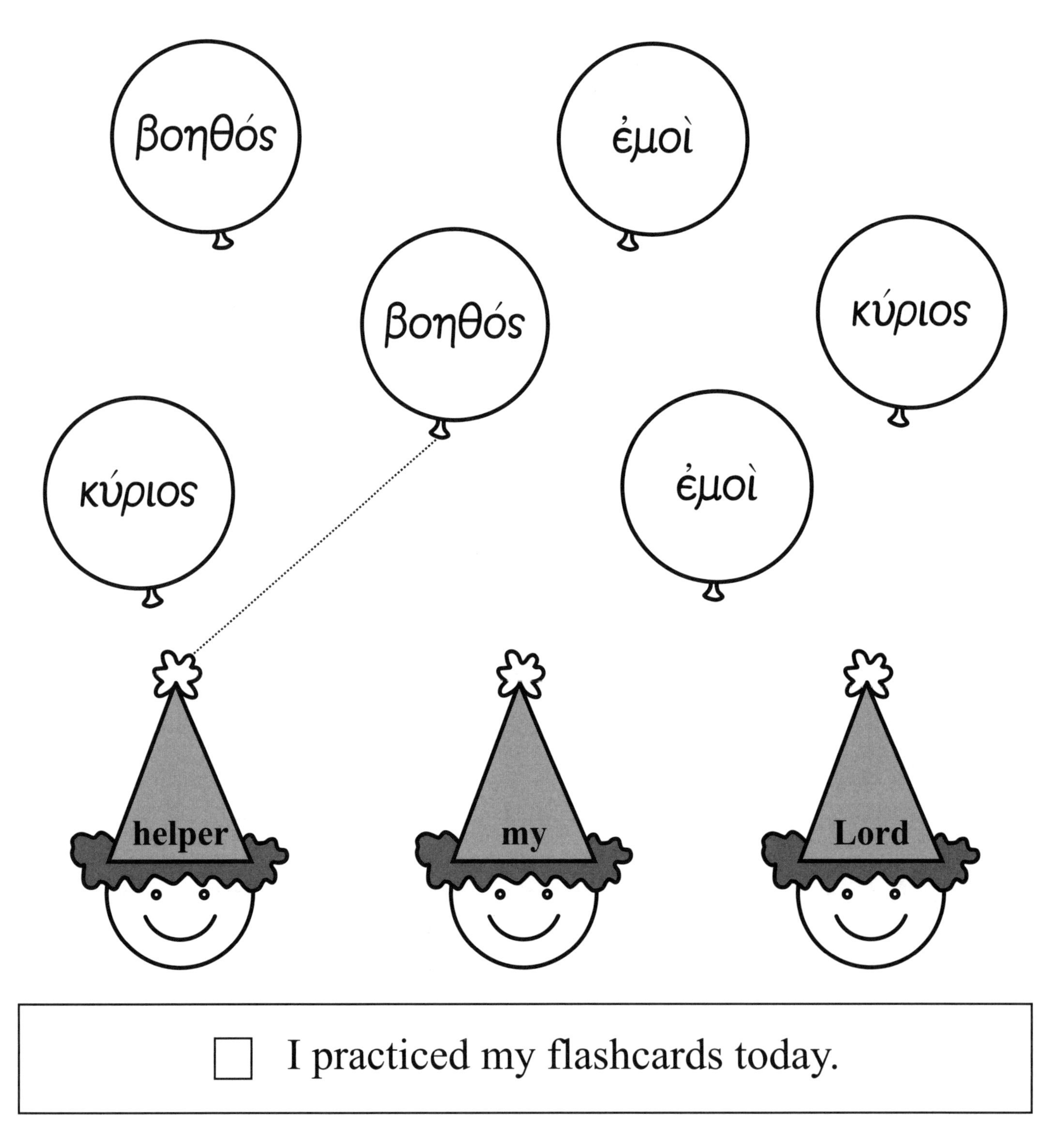

☐ I practiced my flashcards today.

LET'S PRACTICE

Follow the trail. Each time you come to a Greek word you have learned, write it on the lines below.

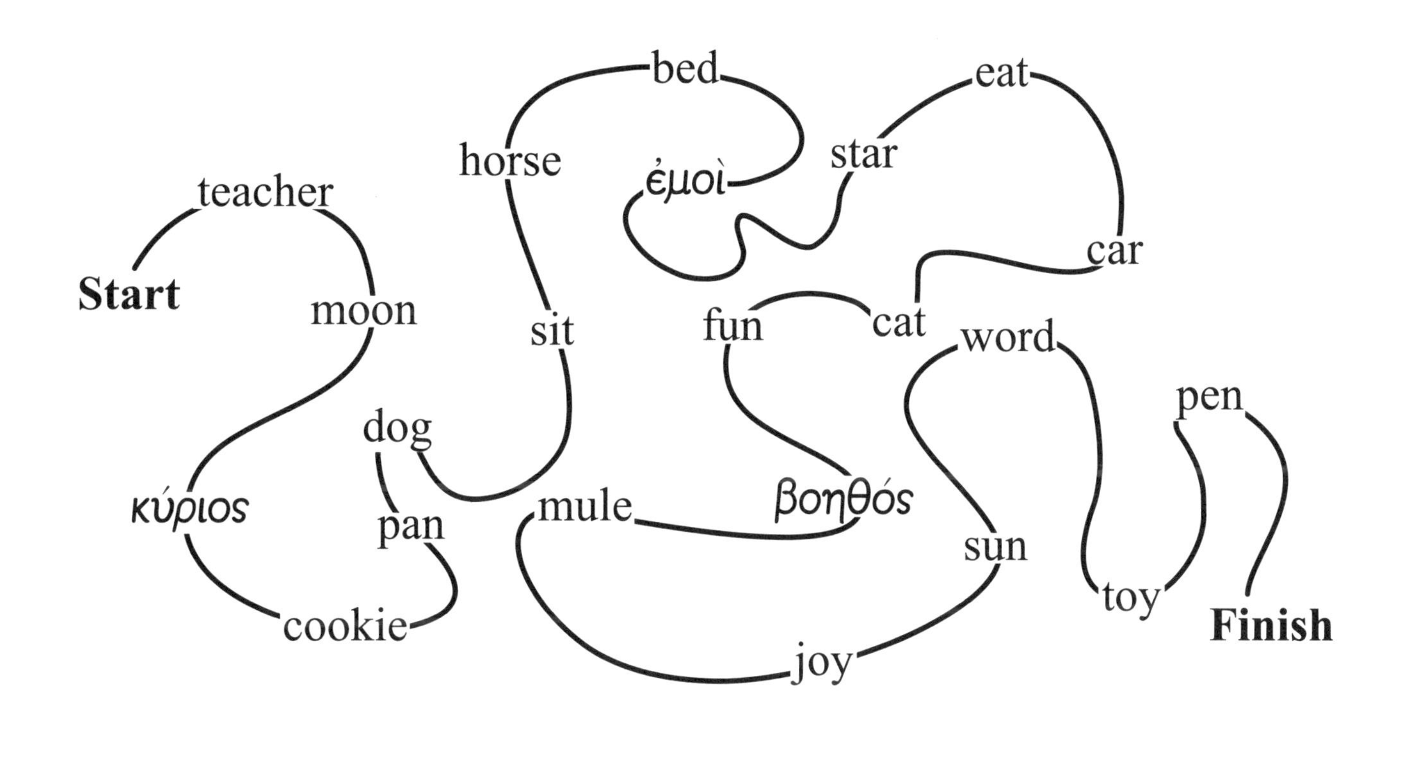

________________ ________________ ________________

CONGRATULATIONS! You just wrote your first Greek sentence. Now see if you can write what it means.

The ____________ is _________ _____________.

(Hebrews 13:6)

☐ I practiced my flashcards today.

APPENDIX

Greek - English Glossary

α
ἀγάπην - a love
ἄλλαι - others (women)
ἀνήρ - an adult man

β
βάτου - of a bath (liquid measure)
βιβλίον - a book
βίβλου - of a book
βλέπω - I see
βοηθός - a helper
βόσκω - I feed

γ
γέγοναν - they became
γίνομαι - I become
γογγύζω - I mutter
γραφή - a writing
γράφω - I write
γυνή - a married woman

δ
δέω - I bind
διδάσκω - I teach
δίδωμι - I give
διώκω - I pursue
δολόω - I bait

ε
ἐμοί - my
ἑτέρου - of another
εὑρέθη - he was found
ἔχω - I have

ζ
ζήλου - of a zeal
ζόφον - a thick darkness
ζώνη - a zone

η
ἥκω - I have arrived
ἠνοίγη - it was opened
ἤχθη - he was led

θ
θέσθε - (you) put
θηρίον - a wild animal
θύρα - a door, a gate

ι
ἰδίων - of one's own
ἰσχύν - a strength

κ
καθότι - according as
κέκληκε - he has called
κλίνω - I bow down
κόκκον - a kernel, a grain, a seed
κύριος - Lord
κύων - a dog
κωφόν - blunt, dull

μ
μέλι - honey
μύρον - an ointment

π
πέντε - five
πέπωκε - he has drunk
πέριξ - round about

ρ
ῥαντίζω - I sprinkle
ῥήγνυμι - I rend
ῥίπτω - I hurl, I throw, I cast

σ
σινδών - fine linen
σκηνήν - a tent
στάσιν - a standing or dignity

τ
ταῦτα - the same things
τίκτω - I bear
τρίτη - third

APPENDIX

Greek Alphabet

Capital Letter	Small Letter	Name	Pronunciation
Α	α	alpha (**al**-fa)	**a** in *father*
Β	β	beta (**bay**-ta)	**b** in *bat*
Γ	γ	gamma (**gam**-ma)	**g** in *God*
Δ	δ	delta (**del**-ta)	**d** in *dog*
Ε	ε	epsilon (**ep**-si-lon)	**e** in *get*
Ζ	ζ	zeta (**zay**-ta)	**dz** in *adze*
Η	η	eta (**ay**-ta)	**a** in *late*
Θ	θ	theta (**thay**-ta)	**th** in *bath*
Ι	ι	iota (ee-**o**-ta)	**i** in *pit*
Κ	κ	kappa (**kap**-pa)	**k** in *kite*
Λ	λ	lambda (**lamb**-da)	**l** in *lamb*
Μ	μ	mu (moo)	**m** in *man*
Ν	ν	nu (noo)	**n** in *nice*
Ξ	ξ	xi (ksee)	**x** in *box*
Ο	ο	omicron (**ahm**-i-cron)	**o** in *obey**
Π	π	pi (pie)	**p** in *pie*
Ρ	ρ	rho (row)	**r** in *row*
Σ	σ ς	sigma (**sig**-ma)	**s** in *sit*
Τ	τ	tau (tou)	**t** in *toy*
Υ	υ	upsilon (**up**-si-lon)	**oo** in *good*
Φ	φ	phi (fee)	**f** in *fun*
Χ	χ	chi (kee)	**ch** in *Ach*
Ψ	ψ	psi (psee)	**ps** in *lips*
Ω	ω	omega (o-**may**-ga)	**o** in *note**

*The ο and the ω both have a long o sound, but the ω is held longer.

Vowels and Diphthongs

Short Vowels:

α	**a** in ***father***
ε	**e** in ***get***
ο	**o** in ***obey***
ι	**i** in ***pit***
υ	**oo** in ***good***

Long Vowels:

α	**a** in ***father***, but held longer
η	**a** in ***late***
ω	**o** in ***note***
ι	**ee** in ***feet***
υ	**oo** in ***good***, but held longer

Most common Greek diphthongs:

αι	**ai** in ***aisle***
ει	**a** in ***fate*** (same sound as η)
οι	**oi** in ***oil***
αυ	**ow** in ***cow***
ευ	**eu** in ***feud***
ου	**oo** in ***food***
υι	**uee** in ***queen***

(Note: A diphthong combines two vowels into one syllable. For example, the **oi** in our English word **boil** is a diphthong.)

When an iota (ι) follows certain long vowels (α, η, ω), it is written below the letter instead of after it (ᾳ, ῃ, ῳ). This is called an **iota subscript**. These diphthongs sound the same as the long vowels alone.

APPENDIX

Flashcard Tips

1. Remember to practice flashcards daily.
2. Do not move ahead in the workbook if your student is struggling for mastery. Review the flashcards every day until your student is confident and ready to learn more.

(front)	(back)
α	(Page 1) (Level 1) alpha
β	(Page 5) (Level 1) beta
γ	(Page 9) (Level 1) gamma
δ	(Page 13) (Level 1) delta
ϵ	(Page 17) (Level 1) epsilon
ζ	(Page 21) (Level 1) zeta

(front)	(back)
η	(Page 25) (Level 1) eta
θ	(Page 29) (Level 1) theta
ι	(Page 33) (Level 1) iota
κ	(Page 37) (Level 1) kappa
λ	(Page 41) (Level 1) lambda
μ	(Page 45) (Level 1) mu

(front)	(back)
ν	(Page 49) (Level 1) nu
ξ	(Page 53) (Level 1) xi
ο	(Page 57) (Level 1) omicron
π	(Page 61) (Level 1) pi
ρ	(Page 65) (Level 1) rho
σ	(Page 69) (Level 1) sigma

(front)	(back)
ς	(Page 69) (Level 1) sigma
τ	(Page 73) (Level 1) tau
υ	(Page 77) (Level 1) upsilon
ϕ	(Page 81) (Level 1) phi
χ	(Page 85) (Level 1) chi
ψ	(Page 89) (Level 1) psi

(front)	(back)
ω	(Page 93) (Level 1) omega
κύριος	(Page 97) (Level 1) Lord
ἐμοὶ	(Page 99) (Level 1) my
βοηθός	(Page 103) (Level 1) helper